Neil Munro's
JIMMY SWAN

14 William Street, Greenock PA15 1BT.
Tel: (0475) 26198.

First Published: 1931, Wm.Blackwood, Edinburgh.
Original Material: Seanachaidh Publishing Ltd., 1988
Design and Illustrations: Seanachaidh Publishing Ltd., 1988.

ISBN: 0 948963 40 9

Cover Illustration by Jim Hamilton.
Cover Design/Illustrations by Stephen Kennedy.

Printed by: Bell and Bain Ltd.,Glasgow.

JIMMY SWAN

CONTENTS

Other Titles By Seanachaidh Publishing Ltd:

Para Handy (Illustrated)
The Very Best of Para Handy (Twin Cassette)
Erchie
C'mon Geeze Yer Patter!
C'mon Geeze Yer Patter (Cassette)
Voyages of the Vital Spark
Folklore of the Scots
Legends of the Clans
Giants of Loch Shiel and other Scottish Tales
The Fairy Mound and other Scottish Tales

The above titles are also available as STORY CASSETTES
For a full list of current titles, contact the Publisher

THE JOY TRAVELLER

I

STARS TO PUSH

Mr Swan, the work of the day accomplished, stood smoking at the Buck's Head door, and the sky was all a-glee with twinkling stars which are quite irrelevant to the story and are merely mentioned here to indicate that it was evening. And yet, when I come to think of it, the stars deserve this mention, for their shining, so serene and cool and joyous, had some influence both on Jimmy and the story. They set him wondering on the mystery of things and on the purpose of his being and his life.

Behind him in the hall of the hotel, the boots, old Willie piled his sample-cases ready for the boat at six o'clock next morning. The billiard-room seemed full of villagers; the sound of chaff and laughter and the clink of tumblers came from it occasionally. But Jimmy scarcely heard it—wrapt in contemplation of the stars.

From out the billiard-room, at last, there came a man who seemed to have decided, not a moment to soon—indeed, unfortunately, too late—that it was time for home. He fumbled for his top-coat, hanging with a dozen others on a stand, and he was forced to stretch himself a little over Jimmy's cases, piled up very high about the stand by Willie.

"A fine night, Mr Sloan," said Jimmy, who knew even recent incomers to Birrelton; and he helped him put on his coat.

"There's naething wrang wi' the night," said Mr Sloan, "except for thae damn bags o' yours. . . Perf'ly rideec'lous! A body might as weel be on a steamer. . . Shouldn' be allowed!" He was at that particular stage of fermentation where the scum of personal temperament comes bubbling to the top.

"Sorry they should be in your road," said Jimmy, affably. "They're often in my own. It's yin o' the chief drawbacks to bein' what the papers ca' an ambassador o' commerce."

"Ambass'or o' commerce!" hiccoughed Mr Sloan. "Nonsense! Jus' a common bagman!" And the two younger men who had joined him laughed at this brilliant sally.

"Right ye are!" said Jimmy. "Just a common bagman! That's what I was thinkin', standin' here takin' my bit smoke, and lookin' at the stars. Just a plain auld bagman sellin' silks and ribbons! I wish my line was traivellin' for stars. My Jove! if I had stars to push, I could get orders! A line like that would gie me scope; I'm sometimes sick o' wastin' words on Shantungs and on down-quilt patterns."

Mr Sloan was feeling nasty—distinctly nasty, having barked his shin on a sample case, and having an uneasy sense that he had forgotten something, and that he should have been home to his wife a good deal earlier. He wished to work himself into the proper spirit for a lively domestic altercation.

"What hae ye got in a' thae cases?" said he.

"Joy," said Jimmy, rappin' out his pipe upon his palm, and pursing up his mouth.

"Oh to bleezes!" said the man, "you're drunk."

"Just touched a wee, perhaps, wi' drinkin' starlight," said Jimmy. "But still I'm tellin' ye, I'm a traiveller for joy, and there's my samples. If I was openin' up my bags to ye, it's likely ye would only see dry-goods. I saw them, last, mysel' as dry-goods when I packed them, but it just came on me here in lookin' at the stars I was mistaken; there's naething in my bags but human joy."

The young men roared with laughter.

"'Scuse me, Mr Swan," said Mr Sloan, a little more agreeably, "I've often seen ye gaun aboot, and thought ye were in the drapery line; how was I to ken ye were traivellin' for beer?"

"No," said Jimmy, solemnly, "not beer! Wholesome human joy. Glowerin' at the stars there, I was tryin' to find some excuse for my paltry and insignificant existence, and then I minded I was an essential bit o' the mechanism for providin' dresses for the lassies o' Birrelton for next month's Territorial ball. Do ye think ye grasp me, Mr Sloan?"

"But what aboot the joy?" said Mr Sloan.

"That's joy," said Jimmy. "Youth, and a new frock! I ran over a' my samples in my mind, and there's no' a one that's no' a swatch o' something meant for comfort, consolation, the pleasure o' the eye, or the pride o' life. What would life in Birrelton be withoot me, or the like o' me? Man! that's one o' my ties ye're wearin', Mr Sloan! I wish ye would learn to put a better knot on't and gie the stuff a chance."

"Wha's tha' got to do wi' stars?" asked Mr Sloan, vaguely. "You said ye were sellin' stars. Or was it beer? I forgot which."

"No," said Jimmy. "I'm not at present sellin' stars, though maybe that's in store for me if I could be a better man. I only mentioned stars because they set me wonderin' if an auld bagman was ony use at a' in that big scheme that put them twinklin' yonder. . . Good night, gentlemen! I'm aff to bed."

When they were gone, he watched the stars a little longer, finishing his pipe, and then went to the stand to take his coat upstairs with him. Instead of it he found the errant Sloan's.

"By George, I must get my coat," he said to Willie. "I have a pair o' gloves and a box o' chocolates for the wife in't."

.   .   .   .

Mr Sloan meandered home with that uneasy sense of something overlooked, forgotten, and only recollected what it was when his anxiously awaiting wife asked him if he had the mutton.

"Mutton!" he exclaimed with a sudden sinking of the heart. "What mutton?"

"Oh, John!" she said, "didn't you promise me to be sure and get a gigot for to-morrow? You know that it's the holiday, and all the shops 'll be shut. What am I to do for dinner?"

"As sure as death I clean forgot it, talkin' with a chap aboot the stars," said Mr Sloan, contritely, as she helped him to take off his coat.

She put a hand into its pockets and produced a pair of reindeer gloves and a box of chocolates. "What in all the world is this?" she asked him, and he stared, himself, confounded.

"I don't have ony mind o' buying them," said he; "but that's a' right: I likely meant them for a peace offerin'."

"You're just a dear!" she cried, delightedly; "although you did forget the mutton," and she put the gloves on, finding them a perfect size.

There was a ringing at the door.

.   .   .   .

"I'm very sorry to disturb you at this hour," said Mr Swan, "but there's been a slight mistake. I have a coat the very neighbour of your husband's, and we got them mixed between us at the hotel. This, I think, is his; I wouldn't trouble you, so late, but I have to leave by the early boat."

"Oh!" she said, despairingly, "I might have known!" and started pulling off the gloves. "Then these are yours, and the box of chocolates?" The tears were in her eyes.

"No," said Jimmy, firmly. "There was nothing in my pockets, Mrs Sloan: your husband must have bought them," and got his coat restored to him by a delighted wife.

"Who is he that?" she asked, when he was gone.

"Old Swan," said Mr Sloan, half sleeping.

"What is he?" she asked. "I liked the look of him."

"Travels for stars," said Mr Sloan, vaguely; "bags full of joy! Old Jimmy Swan! He's drunk!"

3

II

ON THE ROAD

Jimmy walked briskly up to No. 3 Platform, glanced in at the door of the luggage-van and counted his cases, gave twopence to the boy who had carried round his rug and hand-bag, passed off the latest pantomime wheeze on the guard, whom he addressed as "Alick," and sank into his seat in the corner of the smoker just as the train, with a jolt, awoke to the necessity of doing something for its living. It was barely across the river when someone had produced a pack of cards and Jimmy's rug was stretched between the knees of half a dozen men who played at Nap.

"Come up to Brady's!" said Jimmy time and again, as he slammed an ace down in the centre of the rug and scooped in another shilling's worth of coppers. On three occasions he went double Nap and got it.

"You've got all the luck of the day, Mr Swan," said one of the players, an ambassador in the interest of Dray Gunn's biscuits, who looked anxiously out at every stoppage of the train.

"Wrong, my son," said Jimmy. "Cards are like commercial travelling —one-fourth luck, half pluck, and the balance don'tgiveadamness."

"Bluff, you mean," suggested Dray Gunn.

"Bluff's no use unless you have the stuff," said Jimmy, shuffling. "That's the Golden Text for to-day in cards or commercial travelling. . . I don't care to mention it, Maguire, but what about that twopence? . . Thanks."

"Where's this we're at ?" asked the biscuit man at another station. "Stewarton. By Jinks! I should get out at Stewarton, but I'll take it on the way coming back. I'm not going to break up the company."

There was a young fellow in a corner seat who didn't play, but sat embattlemented round by a pile of magazines having snappy names, like "System," "Success," and the "World's Work." He read them with the fervour of a budding saw-bones studying for his First Professional. Sometimes he made notes on the back leaves of a traveller's order-book. Once he ate an apple, having pared it carefully first with an ivory paper-cutter, and Jimmy looked at him with paternal pity. It made him sad to see a fellow-creature recklessly spoil his appetite for dinner with such childish things as apples.

"Now that's a thing I never could do since I was a boy," said Jimmy—

4

"eat apples in the middle of the day. It's a habit that grows on you till you become its slave. I don't say anything against the proper debauch of apples after business hours now and then—say at Hallowe'en; but get into the habit of nibbling, nibbling, nibbling away at apples at all hours of the day, and before you know where you are your relatives begin to say there really ought to be Some Place of Confinement for unfortunate people with such a weakness."

"It's much more natural to eat apples than half-raw beef-steaks," said the stranger.

"It's much more natural being dead than living," retorted Jimmy, cheerfully; "for there's many more doing it, but hang it! look at the fun there is in being quite alive! I'm not blaming you, old man; I have some bad habits myself, but they're all in the interest of the firm. When I retire from business I'm going to take a house beside a water-fall."

"Man is really not a carnivorous animal," said the apple-eater, "he's frugiverous."

"I don't say that he's quite so bad as all that," said Jimmy, putting up the cards and handing them to their owner; "but he's a serious problem any way you look at him."

The young fellow got out at the same station as Jimmy, who was three-and-sixpence up on the forenoon's gambling, and as cheerful as if he had won a horse and trap in a sixpenny raffle.

"On the road?" asked Jimmy, mildly, as the porters trundled out cases for both of them from the van.

"Macdougall & Grant," said the other, handing him his card, and with the tone assumed by a visitor to Hamburg who says he is in the British Navy.

"A jolly good house!" said Jimmy, genially, though it was a formidable rival of his own. "Good luck to you! I'm Campbell & Macdonald; name of Swan. So you're successor to old Kilpatrick? Good old Kil.! He and I began together on the road in the 'Seventies. Had it all our own way in those days. And a good man, too! Kil. and I would come out of any town you like to name in Ayrshire, neck and neck, and we had the whole North journey in the hollow of our hands. But Kil. had to pay pretty sweet for it. . . . Kidneys, they tell me. Wonder how's his widow."

"That sort of way of making business is done," said the young man, replete with all the philosophy of "System" and "Success." "A man, to make his own way on the road now, has got to have some knowledge of psychology."

"Oh, blazes!" said Jimmy, as they walked to the same hotel together.

5

"What's that? Don't tell me it's nuts, or lentil soup, or something like that. Or do you mean bumps?"

"It's the knowledge of human nature," said the young fellow, fervently. "You've got to study your customer. Don't waste his time. Come to the point. Tickle him with some novel lines. A customer is like a trout; you mustn't throw the fly in with a splash. You must give him the idea that it's there by pure accident, and that if he doesn't hurry up and grab it some one else will have it before him. Once he takes it, you must play him gently, no jerk, no tug, and when you have his order in your basket, get out as quick as possible before he has time to meditate and make it a couple of dozen assorted instead of the level gross. The thing is to watch your customer's eye."

Jimmy chuckled —one of those deep, rich, liquid chuckles that add twenty per cent of his value for his salary. Across the flush of his countenance went a hundred wrinkled lines—the furrows of fun, irony, care, calculation, years, weather, and a little droop at the corners of the mouth begot of that sentiment known as tenderness which may be the greatest of commercial assets. His deep eyes twinkled.

"Man, Watson," he remarked, falling into the vernacular he has always made great play with in the villages. "Man, Watson! I fear you're far gone on aipples! A chap canna go about all day munchin' here and there all by himsel' at aipples without doin himsel' harm. If old Kil. heard ye, he would turn in his grave. Ye'll no' get mony fish in your basket that way, either in Galloway or Ayr. Do ye think your customers are a' born idiots? Take my advice, Mr Watson; I'm auld enough to be your faither: stop your solitary aipple habit and burn a' your Yankee magazines. There's only one way to catch and keep a customer —have an honest liking for him as a human bein' just as clever in his own way as yoursel', and see that your stuff's as good as your warranty."

They dined together at the Buck's Head, where Jimmy was *persona grata*. It couldn't very well be otherwise with a guest who had been coming for twenty years; who had a new cure for the rheumatism of Willie the Boots ("mix the two and take a half-a-teaspoonful every morning in a little tepid water, Willie. None of your hunker-slidin', now: don't put ony spirits into the water") who was deeply interested in the landlady's Orpington hens, and had heard in Glasgow a week ago with joy of her being a grandmother; who called the landlord Bob, and had a rattling good cigar for him; and who asked the tablemaid when it was coming off with her and John Mackenzie. Jimmy, to the superficial vision, might seem an ordinary being surrounded by a rather shabby suit of Harris tweed, but as a matter of fact he bore, for twenty yards all around him, an aura, a personal atmosphere which took the chill from the coldest rooms, and someway gladdened every creature coming within its bounds.

He asked young Watson to join him in a drink; not that he wanted one himself, but just because it is a symbol of liberty, equality, and fraternity. And because he was Jimmy. But Watson wouldn't; he alone was impervious to the influence of auras.

"Good lad!" said Jimmy heartily. "Then have a small lime–juice and soda. Nothing better for brightening up the —what-d'ye-call-it? — psychologic eye."

A little later Jimmy went toddling round to Gardener's, the biggest draper in the place, in more respects than one, and found young Watson there before him, practising all he knew of the psychological on Mr Gardener, who maintained a great aloofness behind a desk from which it looked as if all the psychology in the world and a hundred steam-derricks could not for one moment budge him.

"Here I'm again, Bylie!" Jimmy cried in at the door. "How's the wife? But I observe you're engaged; I'll see you later. See and be good to my friend Mr Watson—one of the best, and a good first journey means a lot for a young chap."

The aura appeared immediately to influence Bailie Gardener. He ponderously raised himself from off his stool, and with a perfunctory glance at drawers and shelves discovered a few items in which his stock was short, though far from being so short as it might have been had Watson been the late Kilpatrick. The science of psychology otherwise had no more effect on him than a glass of buttermilk.

Half and hour later Jimmy came sailing in to Gardener's.

"They put some queer chaps on the road now, Mr Swan," said the Bailie. "I doot yon yin's no' the weight o' auld Kilpatrick."

"It's aipples," said Jimmy, roguishly. "Aipples, and low-browed underground smoking-rooms in Gleska, and black coffee in the forenoon, and Yankee magazines called 'Success,' I'm sorry for that chap; a clever enough chap, mind ye, but spoiled wi' aipples. There's naething worse for wind. All the same, Bylie, we'll give the lad a chance; he'll learn. There wasna a greater idiot than mysel' when I first set out for C. & M. . . . I have a clinkin' story for ye for your next night's lodge harmony."

Jimmy told the story as he walked behind the counter, pulled out drawers himself, and rapidly estimated how much of an order would bring the quantity of their contents to par. Bailie Gardener, sitting at the desk, complacently watched him turning over webs upon the shelving, running through the shirts, and totting up the blouses.

"Ye ken my stock better than mysel', I'm thinkin' sometimes, Mr Swan," said he, as Jimmy blandly booked what he reckoned should be the order.

"It's what ye call the psychologic eye," said Jimmy. "There's a whole lot o' books aboot it."

At high tea in the Buck's Head, Mr Watson seemed unhappy; he had found the town a little unresponsive to the system of "Success" and the other snappy magazines, and in the aura of Jimmy he confessed it. Psychology itself could not have suggested a policy more likely to engage the sympathy of Jimmy Swan.

"I know, old man!" said he. "Dour! I've been there myself. You'll find it'll be all right when they know you, if you treat them like men and not like bloomin' dominoes. Get it out of your head that you're out to sell and then to hook it; You're out to make friends for yourself and the firm. You can't make friends by any process of philosophy, though you may get casual customers."

"And how can I make friends?" asked Watson humbly.

"By being sure that you need them more than they need you," said Jimmy. "That's the start of it. Another way is to live, like me, to the age of five and fifty. And then your friends are apt to be far too many."

III

THE FATAL CLOCK

Dan Scoular, the third man in the Mantles, was to be married on
Hogmanay, and the warehouse expressed its consolation in the
customary way by means of a smoker and testimonial—James Swan,
Esq., in the chair. For nearly twenty years there has been no presentation
to an employee of C. & M. at which James Swan, Esq., has not firmly
rapped on the table with the chairman's mallet, looked round the
company with a pawky smile of the utmost self-possession, and said,
"Gentleman all!" preparatory to a speech which invested the occasion
with almost national importance, and made the presentee determined
that henceforth he should be worthy of the high encomiums passed
upon his amiability, his genius, his industry, and general
indispensability in the soft goods trade of Glasgow and the West of
Scotland. Hundreds of brave and bright young gentlemen bound for
matrimonial havens, or new drapery businesses of their own; for Leeds,
Bradford, London, Canada, or New South Wales, have gone out of
Mancell's Restaurant with Gladstone bags, gold watches, writing desks,
silver salvers, eight-day clocks, or gorgeously illuminated addresses,
whose intrinsic values were merely trivial as compared with that
superimposed on them by the eloquence of Jimmy Swan. They might
lose the illuminated addresses or salvers before they got home, but the
memory of his speech was always a fragrant possession.

For Dan Scoular's presentation, however, Mr Swan took up an
unexpected attitude; he would not consent to preside as usual, unless the
testimonial took some other form than a marble timepiece, and
Scoular's preference was fondly set, as he told the comittee, on this
essential domestic feature.

"Mr Swan's determined on something else," he was told.

"What does he think it should be?" asked Scoular. "I'm sure there's
nothing wrong wi' a good-goin' clock."

"He doesn't care what it is, but he bars a timepiece, and if we want him
in the chair we'll have to meet his wishes."

"All right!" said Scoular; "make it a case o' cutlery. It wouldn't be a
testimonial at all unless we had him in the chair."

So a case of cutlery it was, and Mr Swan agreeably presided. When the
moment came for the presentation rites, the cutlery case in tissue paper
was suddenly produced in due and ancient form, as if by sleight-of-

9

hand, from underneath the table, and Mr Scoular assumed the appropriate aspect of modest protestation and astonishment. As he said in his reply, he had not for a moment expected his friends to do anything so handsome.

Mr swan sent the cutlery on a tour of the room that the subscribers might have the pleasure of reading the inscription on the case, and took the opportunity of expressing his gratification that the committee had selected this particular form of gift.

"For a young man startin' a house of his own," he said, "there are few things more appropriate than a case o' cutlery. You have only got to lock it up and lose the key, and all risk of early bankruptcy due to the good-wife's social ambitions is averted. If I thought for a moment that the future Mrs Scoular was likley to use all that Sheffield steel and electro-plate right off, I would advise Dan to swap it at the earliest opportunity for a sewin'-machine. But what she's sure to do, bein' a wise-like girl, as all of you know, since she has been five years in the silk department, is to place it carefully on the chiffonier, with a biscuit-barrel on the top of it, till Dan becomes a partner. Meanwhile —except perhaps at a christenin' —she'll use the cutlery that's kept in the kitchen drawer. From scenes like these, gentlemen, auld Scotia's grandeur springs!"

"What about the clock?" cried some one in the background, and Jimmy twinkled.

"I was just comin' to the clock," he retorted, dropping into the vernacular his warmer moods demanded. "Let me hasten to say, Mr Scoular, in case that remark has roused fond anticipations that are bound to be shattered, that there's naething mair for ye. There's no clock. And ye may thank me for there bein' no clock; if some o' the committee had their way o't, it's no' a dacent case o' cutlery ye would hae been gaun hame wi' on the Subway the nicht, but a ton or twa o' the monumental sculptor's art on a lorry.

"Gentlemen," he proceeded, "I've seen far ower mony o' the stately tenement homes o' Scotland brought to ruin under the weddin' gift o' a massive marble timepiece, sometimes complicated wi' a couple o' objects reputed to be made o' bronze, and generously alluded to as 'ornaments.' It's a mean advantage to tak' o' ony young woman goin' to stay wi' a total stranger. For, remember, she has got to live wi' that timepiece a' day, and a' her days. Her man goes out to his work in the mornin' and comes back at night after a busy and cheerful day at the counter, and he never thinks o' her bein' shut up a' the time wi' an Italian monument that is for ever recallin' to her the shortness o' life and the solemnity o' the Necropolis. There's no escape from it for her, poor soul! She canna lift it aff the mantelpiece and put it under a bed; it's as permanent in its place as a gasalier.

"The increasin' tyranny o' the marble timepiece has ben obvious to some o' us for many years, but it is only within the last twa or three years I got a lesson in what it may lead to that has made me determined to discourage the marble clock as a presentation gift at ony function I may have the honour to be connected wi'.

"A customer o' mine in Mauchline went and got married three years ago. He was in the U.F. choir and in the Rechabites —a thing that micht happen to onybody —and the choir and the Rechabites agreed on a conjoint testimonial. They gathered £12, 10s., and when they broke the news to him that he was in for a presentation, he said he would have a marble clock, and would like to get pickin' one for himsel' in Gleska.

"Up he came to Gleska, which is the peculiar home and haunt o' the marble clock in the most deleterious forms, and drags me awa' from the warehouse to help him at the buyin'. I did my best to put him aff the notion by tellin' him o' happy homes I had seen broken up through the habit o' having aye a tombstone in the parlour; and I strongly urged a chiffonier and book-case, or sewin'-machine, or a bedroom suite o' furniture. But no! MacLeerie had set his he'rt on a polished black sarcophagus, and would have me, richt or wrang, to a shop where they sell them in broad daylicht without the police interferin'. From scenes like these!

"I never thought there were sae mony ways o' bein' solemnly and distressingly ingenious in the cuttin' up o' black marble! The miscreants that do that kind o' work appear to have attempted everything! It was a pretty big shop, and it was full o' black monumental tombs that were made to look like Grecian temples, Roman altars, Rothesay villas, lighthouses, front elevations for Picture Palaces, tea-urns —ony mortal thing but clocks! Yonder they were, tickin' awa' like onything, and we walked up and down between the plots o' them, quite low-spirited, the same as it was a cemetery.

"MacLeerie had but one idea about a clock —that it should be big, and black, and heavy. He picked the very biggest he could get for the money, and I tell you it was a whupper! It was three feet long and two feet high if it was an inch; had the weight of a fire-proof safe, and was guaranteed a genuine reproduction o' the Madeleine Church in Paris. MacLeerie said he liked, particularly, the Madeleine touch.

"I protested to the last. I implored him, if he must have a clock, to take a small inlaid mahogany one wi' a sonsy, honest face, and buy a bangle for the mistress with the balance o' the money, but he was on for the mausoleum, and he got it! From scenes like these!

"The first time I was back in Mauchline after his marriage, he took me up to his house, and showed me the Madeleine in poseetion. I couldna have believed that ony earthly mantlepiece would stand the strain, but he showed me how it was done wi' brackets o' angle–iron.

"'How in the world did ye get it up the stairs?'" I asked, and he explained that it was hoisted through the window wi' a block–and–tackle.

"That clock was in supreme possession o' the parlour! It brooked no rivals! It dwarfed the piano, the what–not, the saddle–bag suite, and the ancestral portraits. It took your eye away from the carpet; I was twenty minutes in the room before I noticed the tantalus spirit–stand. A more commandin' article o' British furniture I never saw than George MacLeerie's clock!

"But it wasna goin'!

"It hadna gone since it was erected! You see the pendulum could only be started from the back, or by givin' the whole edifice a shake, and gettin' into the back or givin' it a shake was out o' the question; ye might as well try to shift or shake the Pyramids o' Egypt.

"I ate brides–cake and drank the health o' the couple in front o' that amazin' clock, and I declare it was like layin' the memorial–stone o' a new Post Office! From scenes like these!

"Well, gentlemen, what was the natural and inevitable outcome o' MacLeerie's vanity? For a while it looked as if the couple was gettin' on quite satisfactory. By and by I found MacLeerie a little dreich in settlin' his bills, and heard that his wife was launchin' oot in the social line wi' regular days–at–home, progressive whist, and a vacuum–cleaner. She was celebrated, ye understand, for having the biggest, heaviest, marble clock in Ayrshire, and she felt she had to live up to this distinction.

"She found, in a while, that her parlour furniture didna properly match the grand old Madeleine, and she had to get in a lot o' new things on the instalment system, includin' a pianolo and a fine new gramophone. The other ladies in the terrace would drop in on an efternoon and sit in front of the Madeleine listenin' to the music and thinkin' they were in Paris, and because the clock never went, they never knew the richt time, so that George's tea was seldom ready when he cam' hame. At last he didna come hame for his tea at a' but took onything that was handy at a public-house behind his shop; he couldna bear the sight o'his mausoleum. When grocers' accounts and the like o' that came to the hoose, Mrs MacLeerie aye stuck them behind the Madeleine for safety; and of course they never could be got oot again.

"The lang and the short o' it was that she, puir body, died one day in an effort to get below the clock and dust the mantelpiece, and her man, between her loss and his sequestration, was so put aboot that he only survived a few weeks after her.

"It was only then the marble clock was put to its appropriate pupose; the works were taken out of it; and it was re-erected on her final resting-place, where it mak's the brawest marble mausoleum in Mauchline. From scenes like these, gentlemen, auld Scotia's grandeur springs."

IV

A SPREE

Having finished high tea at the George Hotel, Jimmy Swan, a little wearied after a cross-country journey of five-and-twenty miles in a badly-sprung waggonette, sought out his usual bedroom, and searched his bag for slippers.

They weren't there!

The ready-flyped extra socks were there; the shirts with the studs in them; the Cardigan waistcoat; the chest-protector he had never used in all his life; the little "house-wife" or bachelor's companion, with needles, thread, and buttons in it; the sticking-plaster; the bottle of fruit saline; the pocket Bible and the Poems of Burns; but not a hint of carpet slippers.

"I doubt Bella's gettin' a bit auld, like mysel'," he meditated. "It's the first time she forgot my slippers since we married. I'll hae to be awfu' angry wi' her when I get hame —if I can keep mind o't."

He went down to the Commercial Room and rang the bell for the Boots.

"Have ye a pair o' slippers, Willie?" he inquired.

"There's no' such an article in the hoose, Mr Swan," said the Boots, "unless I got ye a lend o' the boss's."

"Oh, don't bother!" said the traveller. "I'll can dae withoot."

"We used to hae a couple o' dozen pair for the use o' you commercial gentlemen," said Willie, "but nooadays naebody asks for them; I suppose it's the new sanitary and high-jinkic education."

"The innkeepers made a great mistake when they stopped providin' slippers," said Mr Swan. "There was naething better for keepin' a customer in the hoose and no' stravaigin' roon the toon wastin' his money in other premises. If ever I start an inn, I'll hae a pair o' slippers, a rockin'-chair, and a copious free supply o' cake and speldrins for every customer. What's the result o' me no' hae'in' slippers? I'm just goin' awa' ootbye for a walk to mysel', and there's no sayin' where I may forgaither wi' a frien' or twa. No man's hame for the nicht until he has aff his boots."

He lit his pipe, and walked through the little town at the hour when the cows, that had been milked for the evening, were released from their byres and driven back to their common pasture. The Free Church bell was ringing for the Thursday prayer-meeting. The shops were shuttered. An odour of burning oak from the bakehouse, commingled with the curious redolence from the hot oven-sole, impregnated the atmosphere until he got so far as the smithy, where a little earlier sheep's heads had apparently been singeing. From what had once been the U.P. chapel, and was now a hall for the Parish kirk, came the sound of choral voices.

Jimmy stood in front of the hall and listened. The combined Established and U.F. choirs were practising for the Ancient Shepherd's annual church parade, and at the moment singing Sullivan's "Carrow"—

> "My God, I thank Thee, who hast made
> The earth so bright
> So full of splendour and of joy,
> Beauty and light;
> So many glorious things are here,
> Noble and right."

Outside, on the pavement, he put in a restrained, but rich, resonant, and harmonious bass. A lifetime of encounter with bleak weather had not impaired his naturally mellifluent organ, and he counted no artistic joy so exquisite as the hearing of his own voice giving depth and body to the parts of a well-sung church tune. He knew all the words and harmonies of hundreds of hymns and Psalms; they were ineradicable from his memory, which could never retain the words or air of a pantomine song for more than a week.

"That's Bob Fulton, my customer, puttin' them through their facin's for the Sabbath," reflected Mr Swan. "Good soprano, capital alto, bass no' sae bad, but tenor, as usual, no' worth a docken. Ye'll no get a dacent tenor in Scotland out o' Gleska; it must be something emolient and demulcent in Italian ice-cream."

A moment later, in a cessation of the singing, he put his head diffidently in at the hall door.

"Come awa' in, Mr Swan!" cheerfully invited the choir conductor. "We'll be nane the waur o' an extra bass."

"Oh, ye are daein' splendid, Mr Fulton!" said Jimmy, joining the musicians, with many of whom he was well acquainted. "Good attack; fine balance; tempo tip-top! Wi' an organ ye would just be as good as oor ain Cathedral."

But to his vexation, the practice was at an end. And he had just administered a peppermint lozenge to himself before entering, to get the proper atmosphere, and tone up the larynx!

"Hang it a'!" he said, "the night's but young yet, and I was fair in the

15

key for a spree o' Psalmondy."

"The minister's for naething but the newer hymns on Sunday — except the Old Hundred to begin wi'," said Mr Fulton, and the commercial traveller made a grimace.

"New hymns!" said he. "New fiddlesticks! He'll be takin' to Anthems next, and a solo soprano cocked up in the gallery cravin' the Wings o' a Dove wi' her mind on a new pair o' wings for her bonnet. There hasna been half a dozen new hymn tunes made in my time I would tolerate at my funeral; there's only 'Peace, Perfect Peace!' 'St Margaret,' 'Lead, Kindly Light,' 'St Agnes,' 'Pax Dei,' and 'Carrow' —there's no' much more in their novelties to boast o'. I wouldna gie St George's, Edinburgh, for a' the rag-time stuff in Sankey."

"Let us have a try at St George's," said the conductor; "No.141 in Carnie's Psalter —'Ye Gates Lift Up,'" and the choir, to show Mr Swan the traveller what it was equal to, proceeded to sing with astonishing vigour and address. The summer shades in zephyrs and in hosiery; new stripe and twill designs; the Mona Lisa corset (specialty of C. & M.), the slump in Bulloch's order, and the rumour of sequestration for Macbain might never have been in the mind of Jimmy Swan; he sang his bass like a soul transported high above the gross affairs of earth, and emulous of the cherubim. In the second part, where the voices of the males asked Who of Glory, no other bass infused the phrase with so emotional a sense of wonder, inquiry, and reverence; he might have been the warder Peter.

"Excellent!" he exclaimed, when they were finished. "I liked particularly the lah-so-fah-me o' the tenors; it's the only bit we can aye depend on tenors gettin' a proper grip o', but a' your tenor, Mr Fulton,'s capital —what there is of it. If I might suggest another Psalm, it would be the Old 124th —'Now Israel may say and that truly."

And the Old 124th it was. The inspiring bass of the visitor was enjoyed as much by the choir as by himself, and when he took his upper B's with a clarity no less assured than the sonorousness of his lower G's, there was an ecstasy in Jimmy's soul he would not barter for a fortune.

He got his choice of an hour of Psalmody —Selma and Kilmarnock, Coleshill and Torwood, and Dundee, "Oh, Send Thy Light Forth" and "By Babel's Streams"; and Robin Brant, the joiner, leading bass, was put upon his metal. Himself a man in his prime, of six-feet-three, he was determined no grey-headed traveller from Glasgow, rather small in stature and slightly paunchy, should beat a voice that had been brought to its perfection by daily warblings, pitched in tone to the constant bizz of a circular saw. But Jimmy Swan was envious or emulous of no one, utterly delivered over to the art of harmony and the meaning of the lines. It would there and then have seemed but reasonable to him that the portion of the blest should be to sing eternal Psalms. The weariness of his journey was dispelled; sharing a Psalm-book with another chorister, he rarely needed to glance upon its pages, he was doing what had been familiar and inspiring for him to do ever since the day the crackle left his adolescent voice, and he found he was a singer.

The rosy face was lit with animation; the shrewd grey head just faintly moved in time to the wave of Fulton's pitchfork; when at "Invocation" he said "my harp, my harp, my harp I will employ," there was an absolutely luscious "dying fall' in the opening notes for tenor and bass which gave the flexibility and colour of his voice magnificent exposition, and he knew it, for he glanced across at Fulton with the mute inquiry in his eye —"Did ye hear me that time?"

"Ye're no' oot o' practice onyway, Mr Swan!" said Fulton. "Where in a' the world do ye keep it up?"

"Maistly on slow trains, when I ha'e a carriage to mysel'," said Jimmy. "Ye have no conception o' my compass on the N.B. Railway oot aboot Slamannan. But to tell the truth, I'm no' much use at solos; I think I'm at my best when I swell the volume."

He went home to his inn with a pleasing sense of having spent a profitable evening. He had not only helped the harmony, but from a copious lore about psalm-tunes and their history he had entertained the choir to an instructive, though unpremeditated lecturette; and pledged himself to Mr Fulton to give the same at greater length with the choir as illustrators at a public gathering when he next came round.

At the door of the George the innkeeper was standing speaking to Miss Bryce, the mantua-maker, one of Jimmy's customers.

"There your are, Mr Swan," he said, "I've been asking high and low for you; I found you a pair of slippers."

I've been employing my harp," said Mr Swan, serenely blissful, "and I've had a glorious night o't, Robert."

'So many glorious things are here,
Joyous and bright!

17

Man! it's a blessin' we're no' born dummies! Good evening, Miss Bryce; I'm just lookin' forward to seein' ye in the mornin'.' "

"I hear from Mrs Clark you're going to favour us some day with a lecture on Psalmody. I hope ye'll tell us some o' your funny stories!" said the mantua-maker, who had the greatest admiration for his gifts as a raconteur, and the traveller looked ruefully at his host.

"She's a worthy body, Robert, but she doesna understand the grandeur o' solemnity, and the joy o' sacred song —if ye happen to be a bass," said Jimmy.

V

HIS "BETE NOIR"

Always, when Jimmy Swan is doing Birrelton, he puts off his visit to Joseph Jago's shop till the very last. The fact that there is a Joseph Jago mars, in some respects, the perfect bliss of his western journey, for of all his customers for a quarter of a century, Mr Jago is the only one to whose intelligence his peculiar humour has not penetrated. It is not because Mr Jago is old, for there are nonagenarians on the western journey who, for Jimmy Swan, are far more interesting than youngsters. Nor is it because Mr Jago is a dry old stick; Jimmy Swan makes a speciality of dry old sticks, and loves to hear them crackling when he puts, as it were, a match to them —the latest wheeze from the Merchants' Club, or a joke from "Punch," which does not circulate to any great extent in towns like Birrelton. To waste no unnecessary words on him, Mr Jago is old, and dull, and dismal, and deaf. Any one of these disabilities would seem a trifle to Jimmy Swan, but all of them combined in a single individual is more than even he can swallow.

Most distressing of all is Mr Jago's rooted conviction that C. & M.'s traveller is a wicked man of the world. He disapproves the knowing rake of Jimmy's business hat, his own idea of a tile being something much more solemn, straighter in its lines, and worn strictly perpendicular, only on Sundays and at funerals. Jimmy's patterned waistcoats, too, inspire distrust; for some unfathomable reason, fancy waistcoats are associated in Mr Jago's mind with horse-racing. And, finally, there is that unquenchable twinkle in Jimmy's eye. That twinkle, for Mr Jago, betokens many things —frivolity, foolish preoccupation with the things of time, theatres, public-houses, catch-the-ten, novelles, curling clubs, and Masons' meetings. When Jimmy Swan comes into Jago's shop, the owner always looks at him askance and troubled, feeling as he felt in 1876, when he was last away from Birrelton, and saw the frightful saturnalia of a Carters' Trip in Glasgow. It cannot be denied that Mr Swan is a first-rate traveller, and in that role indispensable to a country draper bound to keep abreast with the city's silly changes of fashions, but Mr Jago would have liked a man more grave; he cannot rid himself of the belief that Jimmy laughs at him, and sometimes tries to pull his leg.

Jimmy, having swept up all the other soft-goods orders of the town, went into Joseph Jago's shop the other day with a stifled sigh, prepared for a depressing hour and the usual misunderstandings.

Old Jago gave him a flaccid hand as cold and unresponsive as a flounder, and groaned some unintelligible salutation with a hanging lip and a rheumy glance of disapproval on the tilted hat.

"I would have been round sooner, but I was having a bite at the inn," said Jimmy cheerfully.

"Better without it! better without it!" said Jago, shaking his head. "It's a perfect ruination, morally and physically."

"Which do ye think the more deleterious?" asked Jimmy smiling: "the tea or the ham and eggs?"

"Oh, I thocht ye said drink," said Jago, taken aback.

"Not at all!" said Jimmy. "Just a solemn, single-handed affair o' stoking boilers. That's no' cloves ye smell; it's the camphor balls my wife persists in usin' to keep aff the moths. If you were a modern Gleska warehouse, Mr Jago, I wouldna need to go to the inn for tea; I could have it in your room de luxe."

"My what?" said Mr Jago, with a hand behind his ear.

"Room de luxe," said Jimmy patiently. " 'De luxe' is French for a penny extra on the cup and a d'oyley naipken. All the big Gleska warehouses now, ye ken, have tea-rooms in them. The latest tip-top style o' decoration —Louis the Quatorze furniture and Adams friezes on the walls, Festoons. . . "

"Balloons," said Mr Jago, with a crafty look of incredulity.

"Ay!" said Jimmy, to save the time of explanation. "A band plays even-on behind a couple o' aspidestra palms, and ye can hear them quite plain daein' Maritana or the Count of Luxembourg quadrilles just the same as if it was in the West-End Park at the Exhibition."

"It's droll I never heard of it!" said Mr Jago ironically.

"It's right, I'm tellin' ye; if ye want a fish and chips or a luncheon *table d'hote* at eighteenpence, it's there."

"I suppose ye'll have a place like that in C. & M.'s now?" said Mr Jago, marvelling at the traveller's imagination.

"Not at all!" said Jimmy. "We havena any o' these facilities in the wholesale houses, and we just step out and round the corner wi' a customer the way we did in '76 when ye were there."

"Ye're a terrible man, Mr Swan!" said Mr Jago, shaking his head. "I think ye'll never be wise."

"I hope not," said Jimmy affable. "It doesna dae to be ower wise in this business."

Jimmy booked his orders as expeditiously as possible, but yearned to inform this obviously mistrustful mind of what it missed by vegetating in a shop in Birrelton. He got an unexpected opportunity. Old Jago turned again to the subject of Glasgow warehouse restaurants just to see how far the traveller's imagination would carry him.

"I suppose," said he, "they'll have the licence, Mr Swan? Ye'll can get a dram?"

"No fears o' ye!" said Jimmy. "They havena got that length yet. But there's no sayin'; they're aye gettin' on. Some o' them hae rooms where ye can get writin' and rest-rooms."

"What dae they charge for the best rooms?" asked Mr Jago.

"There's no charge at all; ye just go into them and sit down, and tak' your crochet wi' ye if ye like. There's naething more exhaustin' to the female frame than walkin' for hours up and down a warehouse looking for the hairpin department, or for some particular pattern o' taffeta not yet invented, worth a half a crown a yard but sold at eighteen pence."

"Man, ye're a great wag, Mr Swan," said old Jago, with a cynical dry cough. "I wonder ye're no' frighted! I suppose the customers'll come sailin' in in their balloons?"

"Balloons?" said Jimmy, amazed to find Mr Jago attempting a joke.

"Yes, ye said there were balloons."

"I never mentioned such a thing, Mr Jago," said the traveller, and Mr Jago groaned in tribulation for this errant soul.

"Ye did, indeed!" said he emphatically. "And may I ask if there's much advantage ta'en o' the fightin' rooms?"

Mr Swan put off his hat and wiped his forehead. His customer was decidely more distressing than usual.

"It's no' the National Sportin' Club I was talkin' about," he remarked, "nor the Suffrage Movement. I was speakin' o' Gleska warehouses, Mr Jago. There's nane o' them hae fightin' rooms that I ken o'. When I think o't, it's maybe an overlook."

"Do you know, Mr Swan, I canna believe a single word ye tell me!" said the righteous draper, fixing a remonstrant gaze on the crimson dots on Jimmy's waistcoat. "Business is business, and it might occur to you that I'm no' so daft as to credit the shrewd drapery firms o' Gleska wi' fritterin' awa' their shop room, their time, tea, potato chips, and fancy luncheons, on customers comin' in aff the street for a bolt o' tape or a cut o' worsted. We're no' that far behind in Birrelton; just last week there was a lassie frae a cocoa firm in England three days in the Store presenting

21

cups of boilin' cocoa and Abernaithy biscuits to all and sundry. I'm perfectly certain it was for naething but the advertisement. But that's a very different thing from settin' up a restaurant and givin' awa' fish teas and fancy dinners and —"

"I didn't say you got the tea and the dinners for nothing," bawled Jimmy Swan.

"Ye needna speak so loud; I'm no' so deaf as a' that," said Mr Jago. "And ye certainly declared there was no charge at all."

The traveller pocketed his order-book and packed his samples, incapable for a while of further disputation with this perverse and afflicted customer. But he was not done with him.

"It's a lang time since ye were in Gleska, Mr Jago," he remarked. "I'm no' suprised ye're dubious."

"I'm no' dubious at all; I'm just astonished at ye, Mr Swan," said Jago.

Jimmy chuckled. "And yet,." said he, "it's naething to what ye'll see in some o' the shops in London. There ye'll can play a game o' cairds or billiards while your wife's at the bargain counter fightin' for her life; and the warehouse has a creche where the careful and devoted mother leaves her baby till she gets her pattern matched."

"Just that!" said Mr Jago dryly. "Keep at it, Mr Swan, while you're warm. Do they haud your dog for ye?"

"Upon my word they do!" said Jimmy. "They'll keep your dog or stable your horse for ye, or garage your motor-car. They would do ony mortal thing to keep you on the spot; I believe they would embalm ye if they thought your widow would come in at times to see ye."

"Oh, ye're an awfu' man!" said Joseph Jago. "Do ye no' think, Mr Swan, ye've come to a time o' life when ye should be settlin' doon to think soberly o' things? It's no' richt to be makin' a mock o' everthing"; and his voice was full of a quaver of pious grief.

"Ach! to the mischief!" said the traveller in a discreet undertone, as he tightened a strap on a sample case. "I might as well try to talk to a skim-milk cheese!"

VI

FROM FORT—WILLIAM

When Jimmy Swan is travelling in the North, sufficiently remote from the Second City of the Empire to run any risk of being taken immediately at his word, he proffers his customers a Glasgow hospitality which would ruin C. & M. if it were exercised at their expense. But C. & M. have nothing to do with it; the only person who has cause for apprehension, if she knew the facts, is Mrs Swan. Her little house in Ibrox couldn't hold a fiftieth part of the people Jimmy invites to come and stay there. For the last week—end on which there was an International Football Match at Hampden, he had five-and-thirty customers urgently engaged to come to Glasgow and sample the cosiest flat in Gower Street. They were all to come from somewhere north of the Caledonian Canal; customers south of that got a genuine Mazeppa cigar.

Nemesis waits on such commercial strategists. Jimmy forgot, some weeks ago, that Fort-William is on the wrong side of the Caledonian Canal, and instead of simply giving Peter Macaskill a Mazeppa cigar, he invited him to come to Glasgow soon and see the Kinemacolor pictures.

"I would like fine!" said the draper eagerly, after hearing all about them, and the Gower Street flat, and Bella's fairy touch on pastry. "Would next week-end do?"

"Capital!" said Jimmy, beaming with delight, and taking out his diary. "I see there's a fine train at ten o'clock, and the fare's only 15s. 9d. return."

"Aye; that's the fare for ordinar'," said Mr Macaskill; "but there's a special week-end trip next Saturday at 9s. 6d. Depend on me bein' there."

"Good man!" said Jimmy heartily. "If you don't come, I'll be awfully disapointed. Mind and bring a waterproof, and leave your presentation watch at hame."

A week later, at the breakfast table, he got a wire from his customer — "Arriving Queen Street 2.16." He scrutinised it through his spectacles with mock dismay.

"What's the matter, Jimmy?" asked his wife anxiously. "Is Aunty Mary deid? Or anything wrong wi' James?"

"It's naething o' that sort at a'," he answered her. "It's the world that's

23

gettin' ower wee. When I started on the road first, Fort-William was aboot the length o' Malta; men were born, and grew up, and mairried, and were made deacons o' the kirk, and died in Fort-William withoot ever clappin' eyes on a railway train. Nooadays the great Scottish cigar belt is steadily pushin' north till a chap's hardly safe to hand oot onything but Mazeppas nearer hand than Ullapool and Lairg. The lang and the short o't is that Peter Macaskill's comin' this afternoon, and we'll have to put him up till Monday."

"Is he a good customer?" asked Mrs Swan, no way perturbed.

"The best ," said her husband.

"Then I'll have to ha'e a hen!" said Mrs Swan emphatically, and Jimmy gently nipped her. In England, I believe, it takes the form of a caress.

Mr Macaskill came with a reassuring hand-bag little bigger than a gynaecologist's, and under Jimmy's guidance steadily worked his way through all the picture places within a radius of a mile from Sauchiehall Street. He had never seen the cinematograph before; it fulfilled every demand of a truly artistic soul hitherto starved upon pictures in the "People's Journal" and monotonous scenic effects on Ben Nevis. The latest picture houses, where you could sit at a table earnestly drinking tea and eating penny sweet-cakes without the necessity for withdrawing your eyes for a single moment from the thrilling episodes of "The Bandit's Daughter," specially appealed to him; he grudged every moment that they spent in the streets going from one show to another.

"He's like a new message-boy the first day in a sweetie shop," said Jimmy to his wife that night when their guest had gone to bed. "Another day o't would scunner him. I was never so tired mysel' o' cinemas in a' ma days; I've never seen as mony'o them, Bella, as'll dae me for a twelvemonth. I'll dream a'nicht o' horses gallopin' and tenements on fire. I almost wish the West hielan' Railway wouldna pander to the rural districts wi' gi'en them week-end tickets at rideeculous rates; the railway fares in Scotland's far too chape."

"Tuts! he's a nice cheery chap, Mr Macaskill," said Mrs Swan. "I'm awfu' glad to see him," and Jimmy gently nipped her.

"So am I," said he. "The only thing to worry me would be that he might be a bother to yoursel'." And again he nipped her, this time on the ear.

On Sunday evening, still replete with hen, Mr Macaskill, whose salient characteristic was shrinking diffidence, became deeply and nervously engrossed in the contemplation of a penny time-table. Having cleared his throat noisily several times, he ventured the stammering remark that five in the morning was an early start.

"It depends on what ye're startin' for,' said Mr Swan. "If ye're in a club, for instance, five o'clock in the mornin's no' a bit too early to go hame to supper."

"I was thinkin'o' the train to-morrow mornin' for Fort-William," said the guest, embarrassed. It leaves Queen Street Station at ten minutes to six. "I'm vexed to think o' puttin' ye up for such an hour, Mrs Swan."

"Hoots!" said she, "there's surely a more wise-like train than that, Mr Macaskill?"

"Unless ye think the polis have a clue to your identity," said Jimmy. "Is the afternoon train no' good enough?"

"It would do me fine, but I'm an awful bother to ye," said Macaskill. "I'm takin' ye off yer work."

"Not you!" said Jimmy, with genuine warmth. "It's a privilege. Stay till the 5.12 train in the afternoon, and see some more o' the picture-houses; there's dozens ye havena seen yet. Ye'll can easy find them yoursel' if ye follow the croods, and I'll meet ye at one o'clock for a bite o' lunch."

So Macaskill spent the forenoon writing home to his wife that he would be home to-morrow, and by four o'clock he had covered quite fresh picture-places and lunched with Mr Swan. At five minutes past four he looked at his watch, and stammered an allusion to the fact that there was a place called Fort-William.

"There's no use o' ye goin' awa' there the day," said Jimmy, politely. "The shop would be shut before ye got hame, onyway; wait till to-morrow and go back in style."

Mr Macaskill gulped an unuttered explanation that no matter what day he went back he could not get from Glasgow to Fort-William in time to find the shop open unless he started at 5.50 in the morning, and that night Mrs Swan had a splendid pie for supper.

"Ye're just a perfect wee wonder!" said Jimmy, and he nipped her.

On Tuesday, at breakfast, Mr Macaskill said, with something almost approaching firmness, that he must certainly make tracks for home in the forenoon.

"Dear me!" said Mrs Swan, "ye're surely awfu' tired o' us goin' awa' already! I'm sure to-morrow would be time enough."

It shook him. He looked at the plump and rosy little partner of James Swan the traveller; marked the dimples and the genial smile of her, and felt that nothing he could do to please her must be left undone.

"Well," he said, "I maybe might could stay till to-morrow, but I must be there to open the shop on Wednesday mornin'.""

"Good man!" said Jimmy Swan, effusively; "I was just hopin' ye would change your mind. Man! ye havena seen the half o' the picture-palaces!"

Mr Macaskill wrote a letter home to say he was unfortunately detained till Wednesday, and with now unerring instinct for the real good stuff in Glasgow, found several picture-palaces on the south side of the river, where he spent the best part of the day, though by this time most of the films were becoming familiar.

He lost his way, and got back to Gower Street at night a little tired, but adamant in his determination to leave by the early morning train, if Mrs Swan would waken him at half-past four. That night there was for supper the finest brandered haddocks he had ever tasted.

"Look here, Bella!" said Jimmy Swan, when the guest had gone to bed; "is this a domestic house or a sanatorium?"

"Don't be silly, Jimmy," said she. "I'm sure he's welcome; and him a valuable customer o' yours."

"But, my goodness!" said her husband, "if we keep him much langer awa' frae his shop he'll no' be a customer at all! It'll no' be there! Naething for me, after this, but the Mazeppa cigar, even, by heavens! if it was in Thurso!" But all the same he nipped her.

Of course, Mr Macaskill was not wakened in time for the early train; it was impossible, with all that brandered haddock. Mr Macaskill manfully concealed his chagrin at breakfast-time. He stammered and stuttered, and agreed that, after all, the afternoon train would suit him better. There were only two trains in the day from Queen Street to Fort-William. He found he had overlooked some really creditable picture-palaces in the east end of the city, and renewed acquaintance with "The Bandit's Daughter."

That night, Mrs Swan had in a couple of friends who sang divinely, and some exquisite devilled kidneys. When their visitor talked of going on the morrow, she seemed to bridle up, and said she knew he was sorry he had come to Glasgow.

"Not at all!" he eagerly declared. "I've had a tip-top time! Ye've been awfu' good to me."

"Jimmy's oldest friend!" she said (it wasn't, strictly speaking, true), "you'll vex me greatly if ye dinna bide till Friday."

"I should think so!" said Jimmy.

So Mr Macaskill waited till Thursday, when Jimmy casually

suggested Friday as a better day for setting out to Fort–William. Mrs Swan continued to have the most engaging suppers, and said that Friday was unlucky.

So Mr Macaskill did not leave till Saturday, having by that time discovered all the picture–palaces in the suburbs.

When Mr Macaskill got home to Fort–William after a week of absence, his wife was at the station in a condition of nervous prostration.

"What in all the world do ye mean by this carry on?" she asked him, tearfully. "I was just makin' my mind I was a widow woman. Just three clean collars and one pocket–naipkin wi' ye, and ye stayed a whole week! I'm black affronted!"

"As sure as anything I couldna get away a minute sooner!" said Mr Macaskill, penitently. "Mr and Mrs Swan wouldna let me."

"Ye said ye would be back on Monday," said his wife. "And every day since then ye wrote me saying ye would be sure to be to–morrow."

"And every time I wrote I meant it," said Macaskill. "But ye don't understand the Swans, Margaret; they're that hospitable; every move I made to go, they raised some opposition. I believe they would keep me a' my days in Ibrox if I didna summon up my nerve at last and pick up my bag and make a bolt for it."

"And what in the name o' Providence did ye find to do for a week in Gleska?"

"Ye may well ask, Margaret!" said her contrite husband. "There's nothing yonder to be seen but picture–palaces. I went to them even on, day after day, and I can tell you I was sick o' them! I would sit in them for hours on end plottin' what way I could get away home from Gleska without hurtin' the feelin's o' Mr and Mrs Swan. Nothing could exceed their kindness, but they might have considered the possibility that I had my shop waitin' on me in Fort–William. I'm tellin' you, it's me that's the happy man to be home again, Margaret."

VII

JIMMY'S SILVER WEDDING

"Do you know what Wednesday week is?" asked Mrs Swan, with a surprising attempt at archness for a woman who had brought up a fairly large family.

"Wednesday week's a lot o' things, Bella," said Jimmy, brushing his hair in a pensive humour induced by the reflection that it was not getting any thicker on the top. "It's the day I have to get up and work, for one thing. It's the day I'm nearly goin' to lose the train. It's the day C. & M.'s no' goin' to raise my salary. It's the day I'm no' goin' to get nearly as many orders as I think I deserve. It's the day I'm goin' to sell 1s. 4½d. Cotton Shantung at 1s., and muslin one-piece robes worth a guinea at 12s. 6d. It's the day I'm no' goin' to buy a motor-car or a steam yacht for ye. It's the day that's likely to be wet, for I'll be in Inverness. It's the day I'm goin' to wish to the Lord I had gone in for some other job than commercial travellin'. It's the day nobody's goin' to die and leave me anything. It's the day that's goin' to pass like any other day, and me a gey tired man at the end o't. Just the ordinary kind o' day, and when it's past it'll be bye!"

"Tuts!" said Mrs Swan, impatiently. "Do ye no' mind what happend five-and-twenty years ago come —Wednesday week?"

Mr Swan put on his coat reflectively. "Five-and-twenty years ago? Let me see, now. Was that the day I was teetotal. Or was I hame at exactly the hour I said for my tea?"

"Never in your life," said Mrs Swan, with emphasis. "But the 13th o' July's an important date you might well keep mind o'. It's the day that we were married. It's our silver wedding."

Mr Swan gasped. "Silver weddin'!" he exclaimed. "Man, I'm astonished at ye, Bella! Ye're a' wrang wi' your calculations. It's no' a dozen years since we were married; I mind fine, for I was there!"

"And where did a' the weans come from, James Swan?" asked his wife.

"Oh, well! if you put it that way!" said Jimmy. "Well, say fifteen years."

"John's twenty-one, and if Annie had been spared she'd have been twenty-three on Saturday."

"Silver weddin'! my Jove, Bella, but that's a start! I aye thocht silver weddin's was for auld totterin' bodies wi' wan leg in the grave and the other on the road to the poorhouse. And look at us!" He surveyed himself in the looking-glass. "A fine, upstandin', fresh-complexioned, athletic young fellow, lacin' his ain boots every day he's awa' frae hame. And there's yoursel' —Bella Maclean or Swan; first in the Grand March, wearin' sky-blue dress with polka dots; the real and only belle of the ball; good for Wilton Drive! By jings, Bella, do ye mind the time I advertised ye? And there ye are yet, getting chubby a wee, but what an eye! and what a step runnin' up the stair! They're no' turnin' oot the same stuff nowadays at all. If only you could play the piano!"

Mr Swan did not go to Inverness on Wednesday week. Instead he took a silver wedding honeymoon holiday with his wife, and they went to Kirkfinn, chosen, first, because Mrs Swan had never been there; and, second, because there was never enough trade in the two or three drapers' shops of that sleepy village to tempt the commercial traveller to take his samples with him and combine sordid business with the poetic joys of a silver wedding celebration.

"Your cases 'll be in the van, Mr Swan?" said Charlie, the Black Bull boots, at the station.

"Not this time, Cherlie," said Jimmy. "Here's a bag; that's all. This is a special run; I'm here with a sample wife —ah! ye needna glower, ye rascal; it's ma ain. Ye'll no forget the extra pair o' boots in the mornin', and ye needna knock me up till nearly nine; nae hurl to Kirkmichael for me to-morrow."

"And this is Kirkfinn," said Mrs Swan. "It's no' that big, and still many a pair o' sox you lost in it."

"It's no' size that coonts wi' toons on the northern circuit," said her husband, cheerfully; "it's the genial atmosphere, and there's whiles when Kirkfinn is awfu' hard on sox."

She was surprised that everybody seemed to know him as they went along the street.

"Of course they do!" said he. "What would hinder them? I've been comin' here since the year o' the Tay Bridge storm, and they look on me as a kind o' institution like Ord-Pinder's Circus. Ord-Pinder's clown and me's celebrities."

"It must be an awfu' dreich place in the winter," said Mrs Swan, though gratified by the public interest manifest in the lady accompanying a visitor who for more than a quarter of a century had seemed wedded only to a barrowload of sample-cases.

"Dreich!" he exclaimed, derisively. "Nae fears o't! When things get slack they start a cookery-cless or a sale o' work for a new flag for the Rechabites. There's nae dreichness about Kirkfinn, I'm tellin' ye!"

"At any rate, it must be a healthy place; everybody looks well up in years," said Mrs Swan. "They'll no' take many troubles in a bracin' place like this."

"Troubles!" retorted Jimmy. "They take every trouble that's goin' except the tattie disease, and whiles I think they don't miss even that. But that's because they're in the Rechabite Tent, and get the benefit."

"If they're all in the Rechabites," said Mrs Swan, "it must be a very sober place."

"A Tent's no' a tenement hoose," said Jimmy; "it's easier to get oot and in to."

Though he protested business was the very last thing he would permit to intrude upon their honeymoon, their dinner at the Black Bull Inn was scarcely over when the habit of thirty years possesed him, and the first place he must take his wife was to one of his customers. They started out ostensibly to walk beside the river, but for half an hour they never got farther than Abraham Buntain's shop.

"Here I am again, Mr Buntain," said Jimmy, bursting in on the drapery counter. "You wouldna get the usual card notifyin' ye o' my comin', but it's all right. A special line in quiet grey summer-weight fancy tweeds, for immediate holiday wear," and he brought his wife forward with an arm about her waist.

"None of your nonsense, Jimmy," said Mrs Swan, blushing becomingly.

"If the wearer goes with the tweeds," said Abraham Buntain, gallantly, "you can put me down for an immediate delivery. Glad to see you in Kirkfinn, Mrs Swan. We all know Mr Swan in Kirkfinn, but it's the first time he has given us the chance to see who turns him out so creditably."

"Well, there she is," said Mr Swan in his professional manner. "Unique. Chaste pattern. None of your French models; British throughout. Durable. Unshrinkable —quite the contrary. A little dearer to begin with than flashier-looking stuff, but pays itself a thousandfold in the long run. The colours don't run."

"You're making them run pretty badly all the same," said Mrs Swan, with a smile, and blushing more than ever.

"I must say I like the style," said Mr Buntain, entering into the spirit of the thing.

"I should think you do!" said Jimmy, buoyantly. "With any eyes

30

in your head. It's a style that caught my fancy five-and-twenty years ago, and I've never tired of it. This season it's tip-top of fashion —one of those Victorian revivals, you understand; nothing like the old patterns! Sometimes my eye's been caught —when I was younger, I mean —by a bit of Marquisite fancy voile or French foulard, but, bless your heart! there's no wear in them, and no warmth. I don't conceal from you, Mr Buntain, that I consider mysel' pretty lucky."

Mr Buntain was prepared to make the silver wedding jaunt to Kirkfinn a satisfactory commercial proposition by giving a handsome order there and then for autumn lines, but Jimmy resolutely refused to book it now. "I'm not with C. & M. this week," he declared; "I'm with Mrs Swan, and we're on our honeymoon —and oh, by the way, I want to buy her a costume-length of your homespun tweed." And he did it, too, at strictly local retail prices, refusing to avail himself of any trade discount.

"Before we go along the river, Bella," said Mr Swan, when they came out of Buntain's, "I want to run in and say how-d'ye-do to Miss Cleghorn. Here's her shop —a good old customer of mine."

"Good gracious!" said Miss Cleghorn. "Your silver wedding! I would never have thought it, Mr Swan, and I'm sure I wouldn't think it of you, Mrs Swan."

"She doesn't look a bit chafed, does she, Miss Cleghorn?" asked Jimmy.

"She looks a good deal too good for you," replied the roguish shopkeeper.

"Don't spoil her by giving that away," said Jimmy. "It's the truth, but I've aye kept dark about it."

"Five-and-twenty years is a long time," pensively said Miss Cleghorn, who had lived that period at least in a state of virgin expectancy, and at times was apt to become impatient with the deliberation of the local matrimonial market. "Did ye never tire of him?"

"I tired of him the very first week I married him" laughed Mrs Swan, "and I think he tired of me in less."

"I did," said Jimmy, frankly. "And now I'm sure I wouldn't tire of her in fifty years. H'm! Inscrutable are the ways o' nature! I want to buy her one o' these Vienna sun-or-shower umbrellas we sent down to you last month, Miss Cleghorn."

"You're the happy pair!" said Miss Cleghorn, when this second wedding gift had been presented. She, too, had an autumn order for C. & M. in readiness, but the traveller would have none of it this visit, saying

31

he had not his order-book.

As they were leaving the shop she laughingly cried them back. "I wonder," said she, "if Mr Swan wouidn't book me an order for a husband?"

"What kind?" said Jimmy, whipping out the order-book whose possession he had just a moment before denied.

"Just one like yourself," replied Miss Cleghorn gaily, and still half meaning it. "I fancy I could not do better."

"Very good!" said Jimmy, gravely, and he wrote down: "Husband; middle-aged, but feeling fine; not righteous overmuch, a fair to middling quality. Must sing bass, and be a good deal away from home."

"I'll get him for you!" he declared as he pocketed the book.

VIII

A MATRIMONIAL ORDER

Miss Cleghorn was a jocular body, or conscious that she had reached the desperate stage of spinsterdom, or was, more probably both, for a month having elapsed without James Swan implementing her order for a husband, she sent him a postcard with the expressive intimation, "Special order not yet invoiced." Jimmy took it home to his wife for her opinion as to whether his Kirkfinn correspondent was really in the market or only taking a rise out of him.

"I booked the order right enough," said he, "but I thought she was in fun."

"A maiden lady of Miss Cleghorn's age is never in fun about a thing like that, though she may think herself she is," said Mrs Swan. "Yon Kirkfinn's a very lonely place, nothing but the birds whistling, and even they get tired of it. You better hurry up and send the body what she wants before the season's over."

"It's no' in our line at all," said Jimmy; "she ought to apply to a Matrimonial Agency. They would send her down some samples or a likely fellow on appro."

"Ye were the sample yoursel', James," his wife retorted, "and she told ye she wanted something as near the pattern as possible."

"Bless your heart! I canna guarantee an absolute duplicate. There's no' mony o' my kind left, or we're aye picked up as soon as we're in the window. I have no idea where to look for the article she wants. All the bachelor chaps I ken are a bit shop-soiled and oot o' fashion."

"Ye were a bit shop-soiled yoursel', James Swan, when I got ye," said his wife. "But whit's a little Glasgow smoke? Ye were guaranteed to wash. Except that ye're a trifle frayed aboot the edges and wearin' thin on the top, ye're no discredit to your wife and family."

"She may be in fun," said Mr Swan, sitting down to tea, "but the honest truth is that Miss Cleghorn would be nane the waur o' a man. Yon shop o' hers would double its trade in a twelve-month if there was a man in it to give the genuine Gleska touch. Did ye ever see such windows? Tea-cosies and combinations, delaines and Turkey reds, sand-shoes and sun-bonnets; and every noo and then a bill to notify the public o' Kirkfinn that somebody's lost an umbrella. To the mischief wi' their lost umbrellas! It's no' her business to be advertisin' for lost umbrellas; let them come to her and buy a new yin! It's my opinion that when a case o' goods from C. & M. comes to Miss Cleghorn she just coups as much as she can o't into her windows, wi' her eyes shut, and puts what's left in some cunning place below the counter where she canna find it again. The art o' shop-dressin', Bella, is for men. Miss Cleghorn, they tell me, is a tipper at trimmin' hats, the thing she was brought up to, but she has no more notion o' a well-trimmed shop than she has o' operatic music."

"I saw that," said Mrs Swan.

"Then she wants nerve—"

"Considering everything, I wouldn't say that was where she was deficient," said Mrs Swan.

"I mean business nerve. She's timid; wi' the dozen assorted type o' mind. If I sent her a gross o' anything —and she could easy sell it —she would take a fit. So she can never buy so cheap as Abraham Buntain can. Her selection is fair ridiculous; if I didn't keep her right she would still be tryin' to tempt Kirkfinn wi' tartan blouses and silk mitts. But where she fails most lamentably is in credit to the wrong customers. Any kind o' fairy story'll get roond Miss Cleghorn, and her ledger's mostly a' bad debts. 'Perhaps they havna got it, puir things!' she says. Maybe no', but they've got her! And still she makes no' badly aff her business."

"Enough to keep a man?" asked Mrs Swan.

"I'm tellin' ye the right sort o' man would double it. What that shop wants is b-i-f-f —biff!"

"What that shop seems to want, and what would suit Miss Cleghorn otherwise, I think," said Mrs Swan, "is Will Allan o' the Mantles."

Her husband stared at her with admiration.

"Ye're a most astonishin' woman, Bella!" said he. "I never thought o' Allan, and he's the very man. What made ye think o' him?"

"Oh, he comes from her quarter o' the country, and he's like hersel' — ye mind he had a disappointment in his youth."

"Had she?" asked Mr Swan, amazed at his partner's knowledge.

"Of course she had!" said Mrs Swan, emphatically. "Can ye think o' any other reason for a wyse-like woman like yon lookin' after a shop in Kirkfinn? Forbye, she told me —when I met her on the Sunday."

That very night a letter from Mrs Swan was sent inviting Miss Cleghorn to spend some days with her in Glasgow.

Mr Swan took the earliest opportunity of having a little private conversation with Mr William Allan of the Mantle Department, and asked him casually to supper for the following Friday night. "I'll likely have one or two friends from the country," said he offhand. "There's one at least —a lady friend o' Bella's who hasna been in Gleska since the time the Haverley Minstrels were in Hengler's Circus."

"Lucky girl!" said Mr Allan, cynically. "There's been nothing really doing in Glasgow since about that time. I mind of taking a lady friend to see the Haverleys." It seemed a pious and moving recollection.

"Was her name, by any chance, Dunlop?" asked Mr Swan, with romantic interest.

"I don't know what it is now," said Mr Allan, pensively; "but it was certainly not Dunlop at that time. Painful subject, Jimmy; your wife knows all about it."

"She's gey close, the wife," said Mr Swan, craftily. "Anyway, this is a Miss Dunlop. Keeps a shop. No' far off fifty —"

"Prime o' life!" muttered Will Allan of the Mantles, with sober conviction; it was about his own age.

" —Plump. Fair complexioned. As cheery as another chap's weddin'! It's a wonder to me, Will, that sort o' woman doesna marry, hersel'. Ye know Kirkfinn?"

"Fine!" said Mr Allan, emphatically. "I served my time there, but I haven't been near the place for twenty years. Painful subject, Jimmy; your wife knows all about it."

"It's no great catch havin' a bit shop wi' a lot o' bad debts in Kirkfinn. It's the sort o' place where the most attractive kind o' girl might sit on a sofa till it was a' sagged down waitin' for a lad to sit beside her, and die o' auld age before the springs recovered their elasticity. It's the sort of place where it's aye so long to the Cattle Show, or so long after it. When I'm in Kirkfinn, the Boots at the Inn has to pry open my door wi' an iron pinch to waken me —sound sleep's the one thing that Kirkfinn is famous for. That and hens! Ye canna venture to walk through Kirkfinn without skliffin' your feet in case ye come on eggs."

"I aye liked poultry." confessed Mr William Allan. "And there's nothing wrong with Kirkfinn; I sometimes wish I had never left it."

Miss Cleghorn promptly accepted the Glasgow invitation, with a quite unconvincing story of being seized for the first time in many years with a desire to see the autumn shows.

"Glad to say I've managed to fill that line for you," said Mr Swan, turning up his order-book. "Middle-aged, but feeling fine; a fair to middling quality; not righteous overmuch; sings a kind of bass, and is a good deal away from home.' I can send it off to you at any time."

"None o' your nonsense, Jimmy!" said his wife.

"I wouldn't insist on his being much away from home," said Miss Cleghorn, quite in the spirit of the thing. "You see it's pretty lonely in Kirkfinn. Is he on appro.?"

"Not in these goods, Miss Cleghorn," said Mr Swan. "They get so easily chafed. And we don't keep a big stock. You see the whole demand nowadays is for thin fancy stuff that gratifies the eye for a season at the most, but has no' wearin' quality, no body. But I'm no' askin' ye to buy a pig in a poke; it's a Mr Johnson, and he's comin' here the night to supper."

Miss Cleghorn crimsoned. "Of course you understand I'm only joking, Mr Swan," she said, in nervous apprehension.

"So am I," said Mr Swan. "I'm the jokingest wee chap! Amn't I, Bella?"

.   .   .   .

When Mr and Mrs Swan retired to their bedroom that night, they sat down and laughed as heartily as consideration for the feelings of their guest next door would allow.

"My! didn't she get a start when she saw it was Will Allan?" said Mrs Swan.

"But did ye notice Will?" asked Jimmy, almost suffocated with suppressed amusement. "I understood it was a Miss Dunlop,' says he, gaspin'. 'My mistake!' says I, 'the right name slipped my memory! Miss Cleghorn's up for autumn bargains; I had no idea that ye kent her.'"

"And they quarelled twenty years ago!" said Mrs Swan, tremulous with the thought of the still romantic possibilities of life. "She told me all about it in Kirkfinn."

"Have ye any idea what about?" her husband asked.

"She told me," replied Mrs Swan in a paroxysm of restrained merriment. "You could never guess! It was because he would insist on partin' his hair in the middle! She considered it looked frivolous. And now —oh, Jimmy, I'm sore with laughing! —now he hasn't enough to part one way or another any more than yourself!"

"Tuts!" said Jimmy, rubbing his head. "A trifle like that! No wonder they made it up again so easily! I'm sort of vexed for C. & M.; they look like losin' a first-rate man in the Mantles."

IX

A GREAT NIGHT

There are villages to which Jimmy Swan goes, burdened with all his sample-cases, as conscientiously as if he were visiting a metropolis, though it might appear that the profits on the orders he secures will hardly pay for the post-hiring. Among them is Birrelton, which is so unimportant that it isn't given on the maps. When C. & M.'s ambassador of commerce puts his cases down in front of the only draper's shop in Birrelton, as he does twice a year, the whole vehicular traffic of the Main (and only) Street is diverted up the lane behind the smithy, and the populace realise that the long familiar range of tweeds, prints, winceys, voils, and under-skirts in Dawson's window will be completely changed in a week or two in harmony with prevailing modes in Glasgow, London, Paris. Though their husbands don't suspect it, it is Jimmy Swan who dictates what the Birrelton women wear —at all events, the fabric and the pattern of it; Mr Dawson meekly leaves all the questions of aesthetics to the traveller, who postponed the era of crêpe de chine and ninon in Birrelton (it is said) for several years.

"About them foulards?" Mr Dawson asks with diffidence, lest their suggestion might appear presumptuous.

"Foulards are no' use for Birrelton; that's the stuff for you!" says Jimmy; and so it is.

Jimmy "takes in" Birrelton, not for any great profit in the place itself, but because it is on the road to several other important places. An hour of exposition and advice for Mr Dawson; another hour to rest the horses and refresh himself, and Jimmy is on the road again, in the heavily-laden deep-sea wagonette himself and his cases call for.

Last week, however, a foundered horse broke down entirely under the stress of snowy weather, and the traveller found himself for the first time in his life compelled to stay a night in Birrelton. Its sleepiness lay heavy on his urban soul, and early in the afternoon he suggested to Mr Dawson that the village badly wanted cheering up in some way.

"It's aye a quiet time o' year here," said Dawson apologetically. "And there's naething on till Friday week, when we hae a Parish Council meetin'."

"I'm no' goin' to wait for that," said Jimmy. "Could ye no' get up a concert in the aid o' something?"

"A concert!" exclaimed the draper. "There hasna been a concert here since Watty Sharp brought hame his gramophone."

"Has he got it yet?" asked Jimmy. "We could hae a tip-top concert, wi' a gramophone for the nucleus."

As a result of active and immediate steps on the part of Mr Dawson and the traveller, the village bellman announced a Grand Concert in the Schoolroom at Eight o'clock that evening. James Swan, Esq., in the Chair. Collection in Silver in aid of Poor Coal Fund.

The school was crowded.

"Ladies and gentlemen," said the Chairman, standing up at a table furnished with a gramophone, a jug of water, and a tumbler, "the town of Birrelton has long been celebrated for its local talent in the music line. A bush is about the very worst place on earth you could keep a talent under; the Bible says you should keep it on the house-tops. Look at Paderewski! Look at Madame Melba! But, passing on, I would ask your kind attention for a programme more than usually rich and varied in its items, a programme second to none, as I might say. Our object, I may say without fear of contradiction, is a worthy one —to do a little for the Poor Coal Fund of Birrelton. The poor, as we know, we have always with us, and coals were never dearer. I will now ask Mr Duncan Tod to favour us with 'Scotland Yet!'"

The audience sat in petrified ecstasy while Mr Tod, the shoemaker, sang "Scotland Yet!" in a high falsetto voice, impaired to a sad degree by difficulties of respiration and a nervousness which brought the perspiration to his brow, and compelled him constantly to dry the palms of his hands on a handkerchief whose more legitimate purpose was gently to wave in time with the refrain, in which the audience joined with the encouragement and example of Mr Swan. Mr Tod was apparently a sufferer from asthma; at every bar there was a distinct interval in which, with pursed lips, he noisily recovered all his wind, which had apparently receded into the profoundest depths of his anatomy; his efforts seemed to be attended with the utmost physical and mental agony.

"Thank heaven, that's bye!" he audibly remarked when he was done, and resolutely refused to grant an encore, a desire for which is manifested by a Birrelton audience by whistling.

"We have a long programme," announced the Chairman, "and recalls must be strictly discouraged, but if time permits we may have a chance later on to hear Mr Tod, whose rendition of that fine old song shows us the stuff he is made of. Now we will be favoured by Mr George Steele of the Driepps —'Aft, aft hae I Pondered,' or 'Memories Dear.'"

Mr Steele, wearing an extraordinary suit of checks, which made him distinctly perceptible to the naked eye, dragged himself reluctantly to his feet at the very rear of the audience, came slowly forward, encouraged by exclamations of "Good old Geordie!" by the younger members of the company; cleared his throat loudly and carefully in a manner that almost amounted to ostentation; fixed a baleful glance upon a high and distant corner of the room, and kept it immovably directed there while he sang —

> "Aft, aft, as I ponder on the days o' my childhood,
> The days yince so happy —Oh come back again!
> When I pu'd the wild brambles that grew in the greenwood,
> And gied them awa' to my wee lovers then."

There were none of the studied and meretricious effects secured by so-called voice production in Mr Steele's performance; his voice was the gift of nature, and suffused with such deep pathetic feeling that he wept himself to hear it. The tears, by the end of the second verse, were streaming down his cheeks; in the middle of the third verse he broke down completely, overcome by his emotions, and abruptly sought his seat again with the remark, "As shair as daith, chaps, I canna come 'Memories Dear' the nicht."

"Go on, Geordie!" cried the audience, "'The Auld Quarry Knowe.'"

In the circumstances the Chairman's veto on recalls was suspended while Mr Steele, bashfully coming forward again, attempted to repress emotions which did credit to his heart in singing the ditty mentioned.

But it was too much for him: he stopped at daffing wi' his Jessie on the Auld Quarry Knowe, and bolted ignominiously for the door.

"There's nothing like the old melodies," said the Chairman, ambiguously, "and I'm sure we all owe a deep debt of gratitude to Mr Steele. But, passing on, I have the pleasure to announce that the next item is of the comic gender —'Tobermory,' by Mr William Gilkison. I would respectfully ask for strict silence at the back while we are listening to our good friend Mr Gilkison."

Mr Gilkison, with a look of ineffable sadness on his face, came forward, assumed a large red-topped Tam o' Shanter, and stared fixedly at a young lady in front, who blushed violently as she rose and took her seat at the piano, which had not hitherto been called into use. There was no music.

"It goes something like this," whispered the vocalist, and he hummed a few bars in her ear.

"What key?" she asked.

"Any key ye like," said he agreeably, "but I prefer the black yins."

After a few false starts, due to an absence of agreement between the singer and the accompanist, Mr Gilkison got fairly embarked on "Tobermory," and the youthful males of the audience signified their high appreciation of its quality by beating time on the floor with their feet and joining in the chorus.

Not even James Swan, Esq. could oppose successfully the vociferous demand for an encore, and Mr Gilkison, with modest diffidence, not too well assumed, stood where he was at the side of the piano and plunged into "That's the reason why I wear the Kilt."

"I rise to a pint of order," said an excited little gentleman at the end of the first verse, and the audience cheered.

"What is your point of order, sir?" asked Mr Swan, in the manner, self-possessed and firm, of the best Town Councils.

"Mr Gilkison's singin' a couple o' sangs I hae among the records for my grammyphone," said the interrupter. "Far better than he can dae them. By the man himsel' —Harry Lauder."

"I am sure," said the Chairman suavely, "that the audience will be only too delighted to have an opportunity of judging whether Mr Gilkison or Mr Harry Lauder is the best exponent, as I might venture to say, of the songs in question. It will be an added pleasure, Mr Sharp, to hear the songs twice, once by the 'vox humana,' and once by —by the gramophone."

But Mr Sharp, considerably incensed that his repertoire should have been forestalled, withdrew from the room in dudgeon, fortunately, as it seemed, forgetting to take his gramophone with him, and Mr Gilkison was permitted to finish his song without any further interruption.

"We now pass on with the programme," said the Chairman, "and as a change we will have the well-known song, 'Imitations,' by Mr Peter Gourlay."

The audience laughed.

"Not a song !" whispered Mr Dawson, sitting beside the Chairman. "Imitations. Ventriloquial. Saws wud."

"I beg your pardon, ladies and gentlemen," said Mr Swan. "I find our friend Mr Gourlay's item is ventriloquial. Mr Gourlay will give imitations."

The artist came forward, singularly burdened with a draught-screen which he placed beside the table. Having secreted himself behind the screen, he produced sounds which were unmistakably suggestive of somebody sawing wood. From the same seclusion there followed what was understood to be an imitation of a joiner planing, and the audience cheered.

Mr Gourlay follwed with an imitation, frankly in the open, without the aid of any draught–screen, of an infuriated wasp. He chased it over the table, up the wall, and round the back of his neck, and finally suggested its destruction by an abruptly terminated buzzing.

"I have heard all the best ventriloquial entertainers of the day," said Mr Swan, "but none of them had what I might boldly venture to call the realism of Mr Gourlay's great sawing and bumbee act. We will now pass on to the gramophone, the next item on our programme. Mr Sharp has unfortunately been called away by pressing engagements elsewhere, but perhaps there is someone present who understands the mechanism. It will form the second and concluding part of our evening's entertainment."

"Bob Crawford! Bob Crawford!" shouted the youths behind, and the young man alluded to, stuffing his cap in his trousers pocket, lurched diffidently forward, apparently with the reputation of being a skilled executant.

He selected a record, wound up the clockwork, looked anxiously about the table, and said, "Pins."

"Anything missing?" asked the Chairman.

"Pins," said Mr Crawford. "Ye canna play a grammyphone without the pins, and I think that Sharp's awa' wi' them."

It proved to be the case; the irate Sharp had successfully prevented any chance of Harry Lauder being placed in competition with Mr Gilkison, and, as nobody else would sing, the concert terminated with a speech, in which the Chairman said that the evening's entertainment had been of the most delightful character, far transcending the best that he had expected.

"Did ye hear what the collection in silver cam' to?" he asked Mr Dawson, as they wandered up to the little inn.

"Eight-and-six," said Mr Dawson. "No' sae bad for Birrelton!"

"Five shillin's for me, and the balance for the population," said Jimmy. "They have a better estimate o' whit a Birrelton concert's worth than me."

41

X

RANKINE'S ROOKERY

The train for Fort-William stopped for a reputed five minutes at Crianlarich, and Jimmy Swan dropped off with another Knight of the Road for some refreshment. They entered a place in the station where the same was indicated, and found themselves before a counter covered with teacups and bell-shaped glasses, under which the management seemed to be experimenting in the intensive culture of the common Alpine or Edible Sandwich.

"They're thrivin' fine!" said Jimmy, peering through the "cloches." "Put them out in a bed wi' a nice warm southern exposure as soon as the rain comes on, and they'll take a prize at the autumn show."

"Tea?" said the lady behind the bar, already with a cup below the tap of a steaming urn.

"No tea," said Jimmy firmly; "I had a cup on Sunday, and it doesn't do to make it into a habit. Say two bottles of lager beer, and —and a bunch of sandwiches."

"Licensed drinks in the refreshment room farther along the platform," said the lady, turning to another customer, and Jimmy and Mr Watson went to the other refreshment room with great celerity, as there was no time to lose.

"Lovely weather," said Jimmy to the lady-attendant there. "Two lagers and a brace of sandwiches."

"We have no eatables here," said the lady, preparing to pull the corks. "You'll get sandwiches at the other refreshment room further along the platform."

"Great Scot!" said Jimmy, "could you not combine both shops and have one regular Refreshment Room, the same as they have on the Continent? It might be wicked, but it would be handy."

"This is not the Continent; it is Crianlarich," said the lady tartly, and Jimmy smiled.

"I knew there must be something to account for it," said he. "Drink up, Dawson; there's the whistle! After all, there's nothing worse than the eating habit. That's one up in temperance reform for Crainlarich."

Back in the compartment, Mr Dawson, who has been gloomily reading a newspaper all the way from Queen Street, descanted upon this idiocy of the refreshment department at Crainlarich as one more proof that Great Britain, so-called, was precipitously going to the dogs. He represented a modest brand of East Coast whisky (patent still), which percolated through the country quite incognito as Genuine Old Matured, and which he said himself, in strict confidence to friends, was so young and robust it couldn't be put up in bottles without cracking them.

"No wonder there's all this labour unrest," he said; "every other day there's some new Act of Parliament that gets you on the neck. It's coming to't when you can't get a bun or a biscuit at a station bar unless you take a cup o' tea to it," a manner of stating the case not strictly fair to Crianlarich.

"Keep it up!" said a stranger, who had joined the train at Garelochhead. "Blame Lloyd George!"

Mr Dawson cordially accepted the invitation, and said things about Mr Lloyd George which it would greatly vex the statesman's wife to hear.

It then transpired that the stranger was a comrade, who had his own views about the social and industrial chaos in the country, and a firm conviction that the most urgent reform demanded was the abolition of all landlords.

"Hear! hear!" said Jimmy Swan, and the Comrade beamed fraternally on him.

"Look at the land round here," the Comrade added with a sweep of the hand that comprehended the Moor of Rannoch, through which the train was now proceeding. "Nothing but deer! Nationalise it, and you'll see a healthy, prosperous, and contented population pouring back from the cities."

"I suppose you will," said Mr Swan agreeably. "When they start pouring they'll be well advised to bring water-proof top-boots with them and a good supply o' tinned meat, for the Moor o' Rannoch's not exactly the Carse o' Gowrie. I doubt they'll no' pour much at first unless they'll no' pour much at first unless they're dragged wi' ropes."

"I thocht you were a Land Nationalist," said the Comrade.

"So I am," said Jimmy. "I'm tired o' bein' a landlord."

"I didn't know you were a landed gentleman, Mr Swan," said Dawson in surprise. "All I have myself, in that line is a couple o' flower-pots and a lair in Sighthill Cemetery."

"I'm one of the bloated miscreants," said Jimmy. "I've been one for nearly fifteen years, but lyin' low in case I would be suspected. You don't catch me goin' round wi' a nickerbocker suit and a couple o' retriever dugs. Forbye, it's no exactly land I'm laird o'; it's stone and lime; at least it was stone and lime when I saw't the last time. If all the landlords were like me, the steamers bound for Canada would be crooded wi' them — third-class, and their beards shaved off for a disguise. . . Do ye ken Dundee?" he asked the Comrade.

"I've been there," said the Comrade, with the air of one who could say more, but refrained from motives of politeness. "I was there last autumn."

"You're a lucky man," said Jimmy. "I had to cut Dundee out o' my circuit more than a dozen years ago, and hand it over to my fellow-traveller, Maclintock. And Dundee was a place where I aye did splendid business.

"Fifteen years ago," proceeded Jimmy, "I had no more politics than a cow; at least if I had, my customers never discovered them."

"Sat on the fence?" suggested the Comrade nastily.

"Just that!" said Mr Swan. "There was so much glaur on both sides o' the fence I coulna' venture down withoot dirtyin' my boots. But I really didna give a rap for politics; I never could bring to them that personal animosity which political enthusiasm seems to demand. When it came to the elementals, I found that folk were much alike, whether Whig or Tory. But the Will o' an Uncle I had in Montrose, ca'd Geordie Rankine, that I hadna seen since I was a boy, put an end to this blissful frame of mind; he left me a land o' hooses in Dundee, and I found I was a red-hot Tory.

"The day I got the lawyer's letter and a copy o' the Will, I gave a dozen chaps in the warehouse a slap-up supper round in the Royal Restaurant, and I tell you the Landed Interests got their hair damped that nicht. There wasna a sealskin jaiket in the wareroom too good for Bella; and I bought mysel' a meerschaum pipe wi' a shammy-leather waistcoat on't to keep it from bein' scratched. Next mornin' I was up wi' the very first train, that landed in Dundee before the milk, and I got a night-polisman to show me my estate. It was the best-known property in Dundee, as famous as the Tay Bridge, the Baxter Park, or the Bunnet Law, he said, and I saw what he meant when he took me to the most dilapidated tenement in one o' the most appallin' slums I ever set eyes on.

"'Do folk pay rent to get livin' in a place like that?' says I, dumbfoundered at the look o' my bonny property.

"'No fears o' them!' says he. 'It taks' the puir sowls a' their time to pay their fines on a Monday mornin' at the police-coort. The Corporation condemned the place to be demolished a couple o' years ago, and jist when they were gaun to dae't themsel's at the landlord's cost he went awa' and died on them!'

" 'And wha's the landlord noo?' I asked.

" 'Some chap in Gleska,' says the polisman; 'I'll bet ye they'll nick him fast enough.'

" 'Will they, faith?' says I to mysel', and I made tracks for the 7.49 a.m. for Gleska, wi' my collar turned up in case I might be identified afore I got to the station.

"When I got hame, the first thing my wife asked was if I had brought a picture postcard o' the property. I broke the news to her as gently as I could, and sent word to the lawyer in Dundee to sell the place for onything it would bring. He wrote me back that I might as well try to sell the Scourin'-burn for a mineral water works. My Uncle Geordie had given up all hope o' sellin' the place in the early 'Seventies. A man that lived in the tenement was factor for the property, and for his trouble was supposed to sit rent free, but he considered he ought to get something extra, him bein' factor, seein' nane o' the tenants ever could be got to pay a penny, and in that way were as well aff as himsel', withoot haein' his responsibility.

"I wrote to the lawyer, then, that I refused to accept the property; he could give it awa' for naething if he liked. He replied that the property was mine by the law o' Scotland, whether I wanted it or no', and that naebody would tak' it in a gift. He also sent a bill o' charges and another for rates and taxes.

"I paid them, and then he wrote that the tenement must be demolished by the Corporation's orders, at a cost which he put at £150. I never answered him, and he wrote once or twice a week till I had to flit, leavin' no address. I tell you I was gey annoyed at my Uncle Geordie.

"For five years I heard no more about my property except when I was in Dundee in business, and then it seemed to be growin' more notorious every month. Luckily it was Uncle Geordie's name that stuck to it, and 'Rankine's Rookery' was never, by any chance, associated wi' the traveller for C. & M. I used to go round and look at it; it was getting mair and mair disgraceful every time, and every now and then the subject o' 'Rankine's Rookery' would be up before the Council. It seemed there was some legal difficulty about haulin' it down without due notification to the owner, and the owner wasna to be found.

" 'Who is he?' the labour gang would ask, indignantly, and the Toon Clerk would reply that he was a man in Gleska, but exactly whereaboots was undiscoverable.

"Then the labour chaps would harangue aboot the scoundrel battenin' on the rents o' the miserable wretches livin' in his property, nae doot knockin' about in his motor-caur and smokin' ninepenny cigars. Me! I never battened on as much as a penny bap aff the property, and the only motor-caurs I travel in belang to the Gleska Corporation.

"The agitation aboot my tenement got so furious at last, a dozen years ago, that I got frichtened, and since then I've never gane near Dundee, in case I would be arrested. And that's the way I'm for nationalisin' property, and daein' awa' wi' landlords. Whether my property's standin' yet or no' I never venture to inquire; to indulge my curiosity on that score might cost me far mair than I bargained for."

"That all bears out my argument," said the Comrade. "The land must be for the people!"

XI

DIGNITY

"The selling o' soap, butter, music, poetry, pictures, or soft goods, is just as great an art as making them," said Mr Swan, chipping the top off his second egg. "I was years ago in a factory where they made Balmoral bunnets. They had a big machine that just fair squirted oot Balmoral bunnets; the yarn went in at the one end by the ton, and the bunnets poured out at the other, a' complete, even to the toorie. I was spellbound lookin' at the thing, and the man that had the factory says to me, 'That's a great machine, Mr Swan. I see ye're lost in admiration.' 'That's just what I am!' says I; 'but it's no' at the machine; I think far more o' men who can keep up wi't at the sellin'. Noo that keps are comin' in, it takes me a' my time to sell a dozen bunnets in a year.'"

"That's quite true," said a man on the road for jams and sweatmeats. "Every year commercial travelling grows harder. I sometimes think the men that have to sell soor draps and kali sookers after we're away 'll need to have a college education."

Dunbar & Baxter's new young man, on his first journey, stirred his coffee, and listened with great respect —indeed with veneration —to these veterans of the road. What roused this feeling in him was the thought that they should have kept their jobs so long; his own beginning was so unpropitious. Yesterday had been a rotten day, and he had said to himself, "Another week like this, and it's back wi' you to the counter, Willy!" It was not a pleasant feeling for a chap who was doing his best. It was all the more unpleasant because there were features of his new job that greatly pleased him —the sense of freedom, space, and personal responsibility, so different from being in the shop; the travelling by trains and steamers; the sight of new places, the living in hotels — particularly the living in hotels. To a young fellow who at home in Glasgow lodged in Raeberry Street, and had no interest in any food he got except the midday meal picked up at a restaurant, this living in hotels was thoroughly and completely quite all right. Deferential Boots and waiters; fish, ham–and–eggs and kidneys for one's breakfast (all together, mind you, and no stinting!); a regular banquet called a lunch, and a high tea quite as lavish as the breakfast! It would be a deuce of a dunt to tumble back from these high altitudes of luxury to the hopeless and prosiac levels of Raeberry Street!

He nervously crumbled a breakfast roll and cleared his throat, and meekly put a question.

"What would you say was the secret of success in our business, Mr Swan?"

Jimmy flushed. He could have laughed, but remembered that he had one time been young on the road himself and full of strange illusions, and being a gentleman he made his best pretence at answering a question to which in the nature of things there is no secret.

"The secret of success, Mr Spens," said he, "is to be born lucky."

"But you need more than luck," said the jam man hurriedly. "You need brains, and pluck, and foresight, and habits of industry, and —"

" —And what's all that but bein' born lucky?" broke in Jimmy. "There's many a one gets on dashed well without them, too; but that's another kind o' luck."

"I'm not sure that I have either kind," said Spens, "but I'll guarantee I do my best to sell Dunbar & Baxter's flour, and I'm finding it a gey dreich business. I begin to think that I'm a failure."

Jimmy puckered up his face, so red and weathered like a winter apple; looked across the table at the lad with a twitching of his bushy eyebrows, and liked him for his unaffected innocence.

"Ye're all right, Mr Spens!" said he with peculiar gentleness. "The worst ill-luck I ken is to be born self-satisfied, and that's been spared ye."

"The great thing," said the jam man, "is dignity. Aye stand on your dignity, and make a customer respect you."

This time Jimmy laughed without compunction. "Man, Simpson," said he, "I'm astonished at ye. If ye had to depend upon your dignity ye wouldna sell a sweetie. Do you ken the way Scotch travellers are the best in the world? It's because they have nae dignity. A man wi' a sense o' dignity is like a man wi' a broken gallus; he's aye feared something's goin' to slip. The thing is to have your galluses right, and then ye needna fash about your dignity. I'll tell you and Mr Spens a story. I used one time to think dignity was a great thing too; that it was a thing ye wore like a white waistcoat, and that the customer liked it. My George! I had as much dignity in these days as would do for half a dozen o' statesmen or a couple o' point polismen. When I started with C. & M. I scared away half my customers by wearing my dignity like an ice-bag on my chest, and talking London English. But I got a lesson, and the only virtue ever I had in this life was that I never needed to get the same lesson twice. For five years I was travelling every season to Auchentee, a place whose only interest for me was that it had three drapers' shops in't. The drapers were all MacLellans; they were all related; they were a' in the same wee street. Auchentee's eight miles from the nearest railway station. For five years I drove up to Auchentee in a tip-top wagonette wi' my cases; and my hat cocked to the side the same as I was the Duke o' Sutherland. I lavished a' my art on the MacLellans: I choked the syvor in front o' their shop s wi' my cases; I flourished sixpenny cigars, and talked through the top o' my head like a man from Sheffield.

"But there was naething doin'! I never booked an order! They were gettin' their stuff from Edinburgh; they had aye got their stuff from Edinburgh, and a' they kent aboot Gleska was that it was on the maps. Three auld snuffy deevils, I mind, they were —the MacLellans; and when I offered them bargains I would lose money on, they just took another pinch o' snuff and said they couldna think to change their house.

"One day I landed at the station, took my dinner at the inn, and ordered the wagonette for Auchentee. It was goin' to be my final visit; if the MacLellans failed me this time, they could go to bleezes. There was nae wagonette; it was awa' at a roup, and the only thing left on wheels was a cairt. I said to mysel', 'There's no' much daein' wi' dignity in Auchentee,' and I took the cairt. It was an awfu' day o' wind and rain, and I had a fine silk hat, a cashmere mornin' coat, and a blue–sprigged waistcoat on. There I was, sittin' in the cairt wi' my cases piled behind me, far mair like an undertaker than a traveller for C. & M., and I tell you it was rainin'! When I landed in the main street o' Auchentee, I created a sensation. My hat was into pulp; I was drookit to the skin; a' the dignity I had could be spread oot on a threepenny bit, and ye would see the printin' through it.

"The whole toon gathered oot, and laughed; I was the bonny spectacle, cocked up there on MacGillvray's cairt, and naebody laughed looder nor the MacLellans. It was the first time they had ever seen I was a human bein', subject to the immutable laws o' nature. Now, folk that get a hearty laugh at ye aye feel kindly to ye after. One o' the MacLellans took me in and dried my clothes; another o' them gave me my tea; the third one put me up for the night, for the inn of Auchentee was full o' county gentlemen. And, what's mair, I got a slashin' big order from a' the three. The moral is that dignity's no' worth a dump in travellin'."

Ten minutes later Jimmy was smoking in the hall with Simpson.

"That's a great lesson!" said Simpson seriously.

"Aye, it's a great lesson right enough," said Jimmy, cleaning out his pipe. "It's a good enough lesson for a young man startin', just to put him on the right lines, but it wouldna be ony use to you. Ye see, I didna finish the story for Spens; I didna want to spoil it."

"What way spoil it?" asked Simpson.

"Well, you see, the three MacLellans a' worked in one another's hands; they a' went into bankruptcy three months efter that, and a' we got o' their accounts was ninepence in the pound!"

XII

UNIVERSAL PROVIDER

There are small paraffin-oil-lamp towns in many parts of the country for which Mr Swan is Fairy Godfather, Perpetual Grand Plenipotentiary, and Deputy Providence. Half of his time in Glasgow is taken up with the execution of the countless petty commissions for his rural customers and their friends, the selection and purchase of goods quite out of his own drapery line. I met him recently in a music-warehouse critically inspecting pianos on which he gave a masterly one-finger exposition of "We're a' noddin'." "For a customer of mine in Aviemore," he told me. "He wants a genuine £16 extra-grand, high-strung, Chubb-check-action walnut one with the right kind of candlesticks on it. I think this is about the article for Aviemore" —and he indicated one with gorgeous candlesticks and a singularly robust tone.

"Why don't they come and buy their own pianos?" I asked innocently.

"They think they could be swindled," said Jimmy, "and I daresay they're right. Besides, they don't know a thing about pianos, and they know that I've bought hundreds of pianos in the past five-and-twenty years. I never bought one for a customer yet that failed to give satisfaction. It's all in the touch" —he touched a sprightly bar of "We're a' noddin' " —"and I could tell the right touch with my eyes shut."

"You must get some odd country commissions," I said, as we left the warehouse together when the transaction was completed. "I shouldn't care, myself, to buy pianos for other people."

"In my line," said Mr Swan, "I can't afford to be particular. I don't make a penny off the job directly, but it helps to keep a good customer on the books of C. & M. A piano's a simple matter; I once had to buy a brass band for Larbert, and a dashed good brass band, too; you never heard a louder! A customer of mine was chairman of the committee, and he said he couldn't trust another man in Glasgow but myself to get the proper instruments. I got the dandiest set you ever set eyes on, and seven-and-a-half off for cash, that bought a tip-top banner, and they never expected the money they had would run to a banner."

It is impossible to enumerate the variety and extent of Mr Swan's private commissions for his country customers, who haven't the time to come to Glasgow or sufficient confidence in their own judgment to buy either a piano or a presentation silver albert and appendage for a young friend going away to Canada. He has taken the blushing orders of innumerable lads who felt the time had come for shaving, but were coy about purchasing their own razor in a local shop. There is no better judge of an engagement-ring in Scotland; and there is a piece of cardboard with a hole in it in his waistcoat pocket almost every time he returns to town from Perthshire. His knowledge of the cradle and perambulator trade is copious, and more than once he has executed telegraphic orders for a superior kind of oak coffin unprocurable in Mull.

"I never made a mistake but once in my life," he says, "and it cost me one of my very best Kirkcudbright customers. She was a widow woman getting up in years, and she had been reading somewhere or other that Society ladies kept their fine complexions by putting on cosmetics. One day after giving me a thumping good order for autumn goods, she took me into the back of the shop and slipped five shillings in my hand. 'I want you to send me that amount of good cosmetic, Mr Swan,' she whispered. 'It's for —it's for a friend.' 'Right you are, Mrs Lamont,' says I, and made a note of it. The only place I ever saw cosmetic was in a barber's shop, so I went to one in Gordon Street and bought five shillings' worth, and sent it off to Mrs Lamont. She would never look at me again! You see it was what they call Hong Grease cosmetic for sticking out the moustache, and she distinctly had one. The best of it is that, so far as I can find out, there's not any other kind of cosmetic sold in the whole of Glasgow than the grease of the foresaid Hong."

The confidence of the agricultural districts in Mr Swan's good taste and commercial acumen is no greater than their faith in his ability to do any mortal thing for them that demands a knowledge of the world, and influence. When the drapers of the Western Journey want to start a son on a career in Glasgow, it is to Mr Swan they instinctively appeal for the requisite advice and aid. No boy is too hopelessly useless for Jimmy to find a job for in the city; the last decennial increase in our population is mainly made up of immigrants to whom he is credited with giving their urban start in life.

"Send him up to me," says Jimmy airily, "and I'll bet you I'll push him on to somebody."

The method of procedure in these cases is simplicity itself. "I take the young chap out to stay with me for a week," he told me; "get his hair cut to begin with, and another kind of cap for him. Then I take him out and start him at one end of West George Street after breakfast and tell him to make his way to the other end, going up every stair *en route* and asking a job at every office till he gets one. He generally gets a job before the third day, just because he is a country-bred boy with a fine red face. Glasgow business men like to have an innocent country boy about the office; it makes them think of what they might, themselves, have been. And the best way to start a boy in life in Glasgow is to let him understand that starting, like staying, all depends upon himself."

The fact that Mr Swan has often bazaar tickets and invitations to artists' exhibitions for diposal gratis to customers in from the country creates the impression that he can get a friend in anywhere, at any time, for nothing. He has rarely encouraged this flattering allusion at the cost of a pair of stall tickets for the pantomime, but no customer or customer's friend has ever failed to get a ticket for a football match, for Mr Swan has apparently the mysterious power of tapping inexhaustible supplies of free tickets for football matches.

"But the nerve of some folk is unbelievable," he told me. "Not long ago a customer from the North wrote asking me to get him a pass by the Caledonian Railway to London."

"Did you manage it?" I asked.

"No," he answered, "I'm not exactly God. The best I could do for him was to give him an introduction to the guard and a list of places that he mustn't miss going to see in the Metropolis, so-called. I carefully explained to him that all the usual privileges in the way of free passes were suspended on account of the coal strike, so my reputation as The Universal Provider-to-the-North-for-nought is not in the least impaired."

Another customer of Mr Swan's found the air of Glasgow so exhilarating as compared with that of Dingwall that he spent an evening in a police cell, and had to send for C. & M.'s traveller to bail him out on the following morning. His peculiar dread was that the newspapers of the city would give a copious and sensational account of the unfortunate affair, which would be copied into the "Northern Star," and spoil the sober reputation of a lifetime. Mr Swan did not tell him that trivial indiscretions of this sort were never recorded in Glasgow newspapers.

"I'll fix it all right!" he said. "You can depend on me. I have only got to pass the word along to the editors that you're a friend of mine, and the thing is done."

There is a draper now in Dingwall who is convinced that Mr James Swan has the British press in his pocket.

But the oddest commission Mr Swan ever got was to supply the parish of Birrelton with a minister. It would have staggered any other man, but Mr Swan set about its execution with as much cheerfulness as if he had been asked to send on a mouth harmonium.

Birrelton had spent some months of Sundays listening to candidates for the vacant charge. Every one was better than the other, and it was plainly impossible to get the congregation into a definite attitude of mind which would give the pulpit to any other particular one. After many squabbling meetings the leading draper, who was ruling elder, said he saw no hope of their ever agreeing upon a minister, and proposed that Patronage should be re-established to the extent of asking the traveller for C. & M. to pick a suitable clergyman in Glasgow.

"So I got the job," said Mr Swan. "It took me a couple of weeks. I knew exactly the kind of chap they would need in Birrelton —not too fancy, you understand, for fear some other kirk would grab at him before the Birrelton ladies' presentation Geneva gown was right out of the tissue paper, and still, on the other hand, not one so dull that he would be likely to be left on their hands till he died at the age of ninety. The minister they aye want in places like Birrelton is a combination of the Apostle Paul, General Roberts, and the cinematograph which never gives a word of offence to anybody, and that kind of minister is not a glut on the market. I did the best I could. I consulted all my acquaintances, and every man Jack of them had a first-rate minister he would recommend heartily for the vacancy. It was always their own minister, and their eagerness to see him doing well for himself by shifting somewhere else was most significant.

"At last I found a young assistant something like the thing I wanted, and put the Birrelton pulpit to him as a business proposition. He jumped at it like a brave wee man, and I wired to my customer — 'Esteemed order will be dispatched per passenger train on Monday.'

"He's a great success," said Mr Swan, tapping his pipe on his boot-toe. "Everybody's delighted with him. I got a letter from the session-clerk thanking me for putting such a fine minister their road, and asking me if I could recommend the best place to buy a silver tea and coffee service."

"You're a marvel, Mr Swan," I said.

"Not at all!" said Jimmy. "I'm only a business man. You can get any mortal thing you like in Glasgow if you have the business experience, and the ready money."

XIII

THE COMMERCIAL ROOM

His *confrère* Grant being temporarily off the Road on account of a prolonged attack of influenza, Jimmy Swan last week took up the Fifeshire journey for him, and put up one night at an hotel he had not visited for over a dozen years. In those dozen years some drastic changes had been made on the old Buck's Head. It had been re-created, mainly in the interest of golfers and the automobile traffic. Its geography was now unfamiliar to Jimmy, who, at one time, could have found his way through every corner of it in the dark. He had now the choice of sixteen wash-hand basins, all in a row; a prominent announcement in the hall informed him that eleven bathrooms were at his august command; a beauteous languid creature, with an amazing rick of yellow hair, put down his name and handed him a circular ticket with the number of his room. "I hope," said he, "it's a southern exposure, and has a fire-escape and a telephone in it?"

The fair being, with a wonderful pretence at talking into empty space, mentioned that the Buck's Head's bedrooms always gave satisfaction.

"Dinner, sir?" said a German voice at his shoulder, and turning round, Jimmy sighed. At that exact moment he had remembered how old Willie Boyd, for twenty years the waiter and boots of the Buck's Head, as it used to be, was wont to welcome him.

"No; tea," he answered curtly. "And ham and eggs; with two boiled eggs to follow."

The Teutonic minion sped upon this mission; Jimmy washed his hands in five of the sixteen basins, in order to test the plumber work, and, still without having seen any signs of a proprietor, walked into the old Commercial Room. It had lost the printed designation on the door, and in some respects was fallen sadly from its old estate. He had it wholly to himself.

By-and-bye the waiter came in to intimate that tea was ready in the Coffee Room

"Good!" said Jimmy. "But I want mine here. I suppose this is still the Commercial Room?"

"No, sir," said the waiter; "it is the Chauffeurs' Room; a Commercial Room we have not now got," and on that Jimmy said a bad word. He looked again about the room; there was the old familiar grate with a glowing fire in it; the sideboard and the chairs were as they used to be;

55

there was no change in the steel engravings on the wall. A host of memories beset him.

"I don't care what it is," he said at last; "bring my tea in here. I suppose the Buck's Head has some sort of a landlord still; don't trouble to waken him, for I haven't got my motor-car wi' me this journey. I take it you haven't got such a thing as a pair of commercial slippers? . . . No; of course not! It doesn't matter; I aye carry my own, and I used to put the house ones on just to please old Willie Boyd. Did ye ever hear of Willie Boyd, the Original Human Waiter?"

"Yes,sir," said the German. "He died."

Jimmy's face fell. If I were you, Fritz, I wouldn't put it as blunt as that," he said. "News like that should be broken gently; the man had a thousand friends, God bless him!. . . 'You must tak' another herrin', Mr Swan'; 'I wouldna risk the silverside, the day, Mr Swan; 'Still the rheumatics, gentlemen, but no' complainin'; 'A' to your beds, now, like gude boys!'. . . Aye, aye! and Willie's gone! No wonder I didna recognise the old Buck's Head!"

He took a solemn meal, and was ruminating wistfully at the fire when the landlord plunged into the room with tardy greetings. "Man, Mr Swan," said he, "the silly folk in front there hadn't the least suspicion who ye were, and never sent to the stable for me! I've been buyin' horse. And what in a' creation are ye daein' here in the Chauffeurs' Room? — I'm black affronted!"

"The room's fine, Mr Lorimer," said Jimmy Swan. "Forbye, I clean forgot to bring my evenin' dress wi' me. And it's still yoursel', John Lorimer! I'm glad to see ye; I thought there was naething left o' the auld Buck's Head but this grate and sideboard, and a wheen chairs. I hear that Willie's gone."

"Three years ago," said the landlord, sitting down; "he was gey frail at the hinder end."

"Was he? Dear auld Willie! slept in himsel' at last; I'll warrant ye it never happened once in twenty years wi' a customer that Willie had to waken for the early mornin' train! . . .Ye've made a wonderful change on the house since I was here last, Mr Lorimer; but sittin' here my lone at my tea, I was feelin' eerie."

"Tuts, man! ye should have gone to the Coffee Room," said the landlord. "It's perfectly ridiclulous!"

"No," said Mr Swan; "I never could turn my back on the old Buck's Head Commercial Room; do ye know it's the first I ever set foot in?"

"I mind!" said Mr Lorimer, chuckling; "you were a little jimper at the waist then. You're gettin' fat, like mysel', Mr Swan."

"That's not fat," said Jimmy, soberly; "it's philosophy . . . I mind on that occasion I asked a customer, old David Graham, to come round to the Buck's Head at night to see me, and it was wi' a gey red face I did it, I can tell ye, for he micht hae been my father. He came in at night, and in a little I asked him what he would ha'e. 'I drink naething but champagne,' says David Graham; 'I'll ha'e a bottle.' My he'rt sunk into my heels; the price o' a bottle o' champagne was mair than I would mak' o' profit on the journey! But the deed was done; I couldna back oot, and I rang the bell for Willie. 'A bottle o' good champagne and a bottle o' beer,' I said to him; he never blinked an e'e, though I was but a boy, and oot he goes and comes in wi' twa bottles o' beer.

" 'I said champagne for one o' them,' says I, quite manly; and David Graham —peace be wi' him! a worthy man! —laughed in a quiet way, and says, 'Willie kens my auld trick wi' the young traveller too weel to bring ony champagne in here. Na, na, laddie; beer's better for us, and I doubt it'll be mony a day before ye'll be able to afford a bottle o' Pomeroy for a country customer!'

"I'm sorry ye've given up the auld Commercial Room," proceeded Jimmy. "I look upon it in a kind o' way as consecrated. Auld times! auld men!"

"We had to move wi' the times, Mr Swan," said the landlord; "I had to make a place for the chauffeurs somewhere, and our commercial trade is not what it used to be."

"I daresay no," said Jimmy. "Neither is commercial traivellin'. Do ye mind o' Cunningham and Stewart, Kerr, MacKay, J. P. Paterson, and MacLennan? Where's the like o' them the day? Kings o' the Road! By George! I've seen a polisman up in Brora touch his cap when a barrow passed wi' auld MacLennan's cases."

"Faith, aye! This room has seen some cheery company!" said Mr Lorimer.

"The first Sunday I took my dinner in't, I felt as if I was in the House o' Commons. Everything was done by ritual; J. P. Paterson in the chair. I was formally introduced as if it was the twenty-ninth degree in Masonry; Paterson made a canty speech, and wished me well on behalf o' the company, and they drank my health. And there was the usual bottle o' wine —I was jolly glad, I can tell ye ; it was port, for port was the only wine at that time that hadna the taste o' ink to me. I've never seen a bottle o' port more ceremoniously disposed o' than the customary bottle on the Sunday in Commercial Rooms. It was an education in the *haute politesse!* At first it used actually to mak' me feel religious! And always 'Mr President, sir!' and 'By your leave, gentlemen!' "

"I haven't sold a bottle o' port to a commercial in the past ten years, Mr Swan," said the landlord. "They've lost the taste for wines, I'm thinkin'."

"Not them! The only thing they've lost is the means o' payin' for them. There's no' mony pound–a–day men left on the Road, Mr Lorimer. And, onyway, port, I take it, is no' what it used to be. Do ye know what I was thinkin' to mysel' sittin' here mopin' at the fire afore ye came in? It was that naething nooadays was quite as good as it used to be. The ham's gane aff, chops are no' so thick and sappy as they were before the Tay Bridge storm, and ye've a' lost the art o' branderin' them. The cut off the joint is no' what is was, and finnen–haddies are completely aff, and there's no' the auld taste to potatoes . . . And —and Willie Boyd's awa' frae the Buck's Head Inn! And it hasna a Commercial Room ony longer!"

"The port's as good as ever it was," said Mr Lorimer with a twinkle.

"Take me in a bottle, then," said Jimmy Swan, "and join me in a sentimental glass to the auld Commercial Room, the memory o' honest Willie, an' the auld Knights o' the Road!"

XIV

THE CHANGED MAN

James Swan had a friend, a traveller in the line of Fancy Goods, who came originally —of all places in the world for a seller of photo-frames and jumping-jacks —from the Isle of Skye. His Christian name was Donald; Jimmy always called him "Donald-of-the-Isles —the fusel-iles," and that, alas! did no injustice to his salient weakness, which was a preference for mountain dew at its very freshest, before the warmth of the still was out of it. He took it in considerable quantities for years, with no apparent ill effect upon a constitution which seemed to be impervious to the erosive influence of moisture, like the Coolin hills or the Quiraing. The parlour what-nots of countless happy homes in the West of Scotland were laden with celluloid jewel-boxes, antimony silver ash-trays, fantastic cats with nodding heads, and Goss-ware, Presents from Dunoon, or Campbeltown, or whatever the case might be, which owed their prevalence in country shops almost wholly to the persuasive eloquence of Donald. He had a way of showing jumping-jacks and expounding the moral value of Teddy Bears that was positively irresistible anywhere ten miles out of Glasgow, his exposition of a doll that would say "Ma-ma," and horizontally shut its eyes was acknowledged to be unique. In Donald's hands it assumed the dignity of an epoch-making laboratory experiment by the late Lord Kelvin.

For Fancy Goods Jimmy Swan had the most extraordinary contempt. He looked (and not unreasonably) upon Fancy Goods as the proof that fancy itself, the cheapest and loveliest of all adornments, was, like porridge, almost obsolete in Scotland, and he never referred to Donald's stock of samples but as "dolls." "Anything fresh in the doll line, Donald?" he would say; "are shammy-leather legs goin' to hold their own this season?" Or, "I see from the Board of Trade returns there's a slump in mouth-harmoniums; I doubt you are losing ground, Donald."

But all the same they were the warmest of friends. It has recently been discovered by Professor Splitzbaum of Heidelberg that the specific organism of alcoholism is a very minute motile coco-bacillus measuring from 1 to 2 micro-millimetres in length, with terminal spiral flagella. In the body of its host, the unfortunate victim of the alcoholic disease, this anaerobe has a curious tickling effect. It tickles the sense of confidence, laughter, toleration, and human kindness, and is the inveterate foe of those pink haematozoa which are now identified in bacteriological research as the cause of self-rightiousness. Thus we have explained the remarkable fact that unfortunate victims of alcohol, like Donald, are often so much more jolly to meet than fine healthy fellows without a single coco-bacillus about them.

Donald was a good traveller, and could sell a gross of mechanical mice with broken springs in the time another traveller would be shutting up his umbrella and fumbling for his pencil. He was generous, tolerant, amusing, fearless, frank, and simple as a child when the coco-bacillus tickled with its spiral flagella; he could be the most charming of companions, and most loyal of friends.

"I like Donald," Jimmy Swan would say. "I suppose it's because he's a bit o' an idiot like mysel', no' a'thegither given up to the main chance, nor always homeward bound. But I whiles wish he would settle doon and start the domestic and temperance virtues. I'm aye tellin' him that if he takes them up in the proper spirit they're almost as much fun as the other thing —forbye bein' money in your pocket."

Unfortunately the alcoholic bacillus in course of time by the assiduous application of its flagella in the tickling process wears them down to a stump, and deprived of its power to tickle to any great extent, it goes ramping round the whole intestinal system biting. An agonising thirst is created in the patient, only to be allayed by increased applications of mountain or other dew, with which, of course, are imbibed fresh colonies of the organism which take up the tickling, handicapped, however, by the increased difficulty of getting a dry spot to work on.

One day Donald came to his friend, Mr Swan, in a quiescent moment of the bacilli, looking very blue, and borrowed £10 upon the touching presentation of a story about a Sheriff Court summons.

The occasion was too obviously providential to be neglected, and Jimmy talked to him like a teetotal lecturer. "All I needed to be John B. Gough was a drunken past, my thumb-prints in the polis books, and a white dress muslin necktie," he said afterwards to his wife, describing the interview.

"Look here, Donald," he said; "not to put too fine a point on it, you're a d——d fool,"

"It's the true word, Mr Swan!" admitted Donald, contritely.

"I'm the last man," said Jimmy, "to say a chap should begin in life by bein' a perfect model, for there's naething left for him to dae in the way o' self-improvement if he's perfect to begin wi', and the later part o' his life 'll be awfu' dreich. I started, mysel', wi' the full equipment o' a first-class idiot —worse than you, but for the last ten years I've got a wonderfu' lot o' pleesure and satisfaction tryin' to be better. I tell ye this —it's far more sport than keepin' a gairden!

"The way ye are," continued Jimmy, "you're just a wasted man! Ye have a' the qualities o' a good yin except the will to use them. Men no' half your weight, nor wi' half your wits aboot them, are laughin' at ye; I'll no' say that they're takin' the prizes you should have, for that's a point that would appeal to neither me nor you, but they're laughin' at ye —no, no! I'll no' say that o' human nature; rather will I say they're sorry for ye. That should sting a Skyeman!"

"There's something in it, Mr Swan," said Donald.

"Of course there is!" said Jimmy. "A man at your age canna learn much more, but he can get a lot of fun in unlearnin'. But for heaven's sake, Donald! —always in the proper spirit! —not too certain o' yoursel', not too self-satisfied, nor too bitter on the weaker brethren."

Donald went away, impressed, and became a changed man.

Everybody noticed it, first of all his firm, which experienced a lamentable and unaccountable decline in the demand for autograph albums with real leatherette covers, mechanical steam-engines (with broken springs), celluloid dromedary inch-tapes, and golliwogs, on the West Coast journey. Donald was blatantly and offensively teetotal; once generous, he was now as hard as nails; once full of fun and kindliness, he was now as dull as crape; once fearless, he was become as timid as a mouse; once disingenuous as a child, he was become as crafty and suspicious as a shilling lawyer. The coco-bacilli, realising the situation, uttered an agonised shriek, and turned on their backs and died.

When he came to Jimmy Swan after a year to repay the borrowed money, Jimmy, who had not seen him much of late, looked at him with disappointed eyes.

"Do ye feel like a bottle o' cyder, Donald?" he asked him.

"Thank goodness, I'm beyond that sort o' thing!" said Donald. "Have ye a drop o' soda?"

Jimmy gave it to him, sadly.

"Thank ye for the money, Donald," said he; "it was good of ye to mind it. There's something aboot ye that puts me in mind o' the smell o' a wet leather school-bag. What way are ye gettin' on?"

"Oh, not so bad," said Donald, solemnly. "I have the approval of my conscience, though the firm is not quite satisfied."

"Just that!" said Jimmy, fingering the notes carelessly. "You're a muckle–improved man, but I'm feared I spoiled ye for a traiveller, and I ken I've lost ye for a friend. I told ye, man, to go about it in the proper spirit!"

XV

VITALISING THE GLOOMY GRANTS

Jimmy Swan, with his hands in his jacket pockets, his hat at just the tiniest angle, his chest thrown out, and his waist reduced by a conscious effort of the abdominal muscles —which things all betoken a determination never to grow old, walked along Shore Street humming "Onward, Christian Soldiers." He was, if you take me, feeling good. The sun shone on the sea-front like a benediction; enough and no more autumnal sting was in the air to give it bracing qualities; he had done a good day's business yesterday at Inverness; had slept like a babe, and breakfasted like a sailor; was freshly shaved to that degree that his cheek was like a lady's; he knew this journey's stuff was irresistible. It was going on in front of him —six weather-beaten cases in the wheel-barrow of Peter Melville, packed with sample lines to make the hair of any discerning draper fairly curl.

He felt as men feel who come with relief to long-beleaguered cities; there ought to have ben a band before him playing "Umpa-umpa-ump!" and a few assorted banners. That was why he hummed, providing for himself a private and appropriate kind of military pomp. Other commercial travellers might sneak ingloriously into these northern towns and go cringing through the shops with self-depreciatory airs, inviting insults and rebuffs instead of orders—not so Mr Swan, ambassador of C. & M., Perpetual Grand Plenipotentiary and High Prince of the Soft Goods world, backed by a century's tradition, conscious of quality unassailable and prices strictly bed-rock, having due consideration for the quality.

In thirty years on the Road for C. & M. he had acquired a Psychic Touch with customers; not only did his stuff talk for itself —why, C. & M.'s trade-mark on a web of Bolton sheeting was portentous as a statesman's speech! —but his manner magnetised, and he would insinuate a new line of zephyr prints into the conversation like one who was quoting a fine unhackneyed passage from Shakespeare. He did not seem so much to seek to sell you goods as to give you the inestimable privilege of taking part with the great firm of C. & M. in a grand disinterested campaign to make the people of Scotland wear the real right thing. No city superiority or condescension, mind you! no bluff or airs! Jimmy Swan had a shrewd appreciation of the psychological advantage of liking your man to start with; of being absolutely disingenuous, and confident of the character of your own stuff.

No wonder he marched into R. & T. Grant's humming "Onward, Christian Soldiers" in his mellifluous bass, while Peter Melville out on the pavement took the straps from off the cases.

He was no sooner at the counter and shaking hands with Robert than he realised, intuitively, that the morning's sunshine and its bracing airs had no effects on the spirits of that struggling drapery concern. The shop looked more disheartened than it ever did before —more haphazard of arrangement, more dingy, more out-of-date. Robert's eye (the straight one) had the unmistakable lack-lustre of frustration and defeat. Thomas, the elder, totting up the greasy ledger in a corner, stopped in the middle of a column and came forward smiling automatically as to a customer, but lapsing instantly into a mask of gloom, his voice subdued to a funereal melancholy. The brothers were barely middle-aged in years, but for long they had indulged a singular illusion that solidity and success in commerce were only for men who looked mature, and they had always carefully cultivated an appearance of being twenty years older than they really were. Gladstone collars, made-up padded neckties, morning coats of the period of the Tay Bridge storm, and — whiskers! And when I say whiskers, I mean actual mid-Victorian side-wings, not mutton-chops, but fluffy cheek appendages, the dire absurdity of which not even a doting mother could condone.

"How's business?" asked Mr Swan, with the cheerful air of one who is confident of learning that business was never better.

"Bad!" said Robert Grant, laconically. "I don't think you need to open your cases, Mr Swan, this trip."

The countenance of the traveller fell for a moment; then he said airily, "Tuts! it's only temporary. Everything's on the upward trend; ye're maybe just a season later here in the North to feel it, but it's working up the Highland Line, and I make out that in less than a week the Boom will be the length o' Kingussie or Aviemore."

Robert Grant shook his head till his whiskers almost made a draught. "It's too late of comin' for us, Mr Swan," he said lugubriously. "Tom and me's tired o't. We're done! What trade we ever had is goin' back. It was never a fat thing at the best, but now it's driftin' over to the store across the street; ye see they've started a drapery department."

"Let them start it!" said Mr Swan, contemptuously. "I'm sure ye ken the slogan o' the Grants —'Stand fast, Craigellachie!' The new department at the store should be a tonic to ye; send ye brisker about your business than ever ye were before; I never do so well meself as when

I'm faced wi' solid opposition."

But the Grant brothers wagged their preposterous whiskers, and sank their chins lower in their obsolete Gladstone collars, and assured their visitor that affairs were hopeless. Thank God they could still pay twenty shillings in the pound and have a little over, but there seemed to be nothing now for it but Canada. Everybody was going to Canada.

"What'll ye dae there?" asked Mr Swan, bluntly.

They would look around them for a while, and no doubt hit on something, they remarked, and Robert's defective and erratic eye went flashing round the shop in a manner which suggested that at looking around in Canada he would be a perfect marvel.

James Swan walked to the door and looked at his open cases; threw out his chest and took a deep breath of the stimulating sea-born air, then turned back to the counter, and addressed the disconsolate brothers.

"Do ye ken what's the matter wi' this business and wi' you?" he asked. "It's whiskers! Nothing else but whiskers! For the love of Peter shave yoursel's clean like me, or start a moustache, or a Captain Kettle beard wi' a peak to't, and be upsides wi' modern civilisation. Gie your cheeks a chance; take aff these side-galleries and look like the year o' grace 1912, no' the start o' the Franco-Prussian war."

The brothers, too well acquainted with their visitor to resent this personality, smiled ruefully. "I see from the papers," said Robert, "that side whiskers are comin' into vogue again. Tom and me's just a little ahead o' the times; we'll soon be in the height o' fashion."

"The height o' nonsense!" cried Jimmy Swan. "There's no wise-like folk gaun back to whiskers ony mair than to the crinoline or the chignong. In either case the women wouldna stand it, and it's them that rule the fashions. Man, it's no' an age for whiskers; ye need a face on ye as clean as the bow o' a cutter yacht to sail into the winds o' commerce nooadays, and there's the pair o' ye beatin' to the marks wi' spinnakers. There's naebody wears whiskers now but undertakers and men on the Stock Exchange that havena ony dochters to cod them into common sense, If any employee o' C. & M.'s came into the warehouse wi' a whisker on, the partners in the business would tak' fits, and the rest o' us would bray at him like cuddies. If the police o' Gleska saw a man your age wi' whiskers they would track him up a lane at night and hammer him wi' their batons. The way ye are, ye're an affront to me; ye're no' a day aulder than mysel', and yet ye might be onybody's faithers. The first thing they would dae to ye in Canada would be to lay ye on a block and clip ye—"

He broke off with a chuckle which disarmed annoyance; there was no customers of C. & M. for whom he had a greater respect —if only they would shave themselves; and he knew they knew it.

"Ah, if it was only a question o' whiskers!" said Thomas, sadly.

"It's ALL a question o' whiskers!" vehemently retorted Jimmy Swan. "There's naething criminal or immoral about whiskers, but in a drapery concern they're a Symbol. Your fine half–Dundrearies are an indication o' your state o' mind. The world is a' for youth —which I take to be onything under sixty, and there's the pair o' ye advertisin' that ye're nearly centenarians. It's no' on your face only that there's whiskers; they're in your philisophy and on your business. Twa men your age, wi' health, and twenty shillin's in the pound, and an auld–established business, should be oot in the mornin's whistlin' like mavises and gambollin' round the shop like boys."

"I doubt we're not the gambollin' kind," said Robert humbly, for the first time in his life painfully conscious of his whiskers. "But nobody can say we haven't paid strict attention to business." . . . "And walked in the fear of God," he added as an afterthought.

"That's it!" said Jimmy Swan. "More whiskers! It would suit ye better to walk in His glory and sing the 27th Psalm. It's no' in the fear and admonition o' the Lord ye're walkin', but in mortal terror o' the Store. Bonny–like Grants ye are? Wi' a motto like 'Stand Fast!' that ought to stir ye up and stiffen ye like a trumpet! Man, the very sound o't dirls like the tune Dunfermline!"

"There's something in it!" said Thomas tremulously. "Perhaps we were a little too timid about the Store Robert?"

"Ye couldna help it wi' thae whiskers!" said Jimmy Swan. "There's nothing worse for the nerve than fluff. Shave off your whiskers and I'll guarantee that between us we'll make the Store look silly. I never saw the sense o' Stores; they don't get their stuff from C. & M."

"Could ye suggest anything, Mr Swan?" asked Robert, also infected by this fearless spirit. "Anything to, as it were, buck us up in the business?"

"Man, amn't I tellin' ye? —Whiskers! whiskers! whiskers! Get them aff! Be as young as I am —twenty–six; I only begin to count from the day I married. It's a' nonsense about bein' douce and demure, and auld–lookin' —at least, in the drapery trade; it may suit a' right wi' undertakers. Take the whiskers aff your shop, and aff your stock, and aff the dressin' o' your windows!"

"There's maybe something in what you say," admitted Robert, "But there seem to be such chances out in Canada!"

"Of course there are!" said Jimmy Swan. "Wherever there's clean cheeks, there's chances, and every man in Canada has a safety razor. But, bless your heart, man! Canada's no' the only place! If half the folk that went to Canada has only stayed at home and shaved themsel's, and took the side-wings aff their business, and the fluff frae their way o' lookin' at things, there would be nae necessity to emigrate. Are ye stupid enough to think this country's done because the Store has added drapery? It's a sign that it's only startin', and that better men are wanted. Good luck to them in Canada! but let you and me stay here and shave oursel's."

The brothers Grant looked at each other. "I think, after all," said Thomas, "you might show us some of your winter lines."

"Certainly," said Jimmy Swan with the upmost alacrity, and humming "Onward, Christian Soldiers," went outside to fetch his samples.

XVI

BLATE RACHEL

Jimmy Swan, with a superb carnation in his coat-lapel, was leaning on the counter of the widow Thorpe, recounting all the splendours of a wedding he had been a guest at on the previous day, when he observed a tear was in the widow's eye. He promptly changed the subject, and went back to the claims of Union Shantung for good hard wear and smart appearance. "You never can tell," he thought, "when a widow woman's too far on in years to be sentimental; the puir old body's envious." But he misunderstood.

"Everybody has luck but me," she said to him, indifferent, for the moment, to his Shantung samples; "there's my lassie Rachel, and there's no' a man looks near her."

"Toots!" said Jimmy blithely, "what's the matter wi' her? Is she skelly-e'ed?"

"There's naething wrang wi' her," replied the widow peevishly; "she got a better chance, to start wi', in her looks than ever I got, but she's blate. Put her next a lad, and she's so shy she might be skelly in both e'es and he wouldna get a chance to see it."

"Blate!" said Jimmy, with surprise. "That's a female disease I thought was oot o' fashion. Are ye sure it's no' her adenoids?"

The widow positively wept as she disclosed the troubles she had had with Rachel. She had given her a first-rate-education, up as far as Chemistry and Elocution; she had lavished dress upon her to the point of gold watch-wristlets, petticoats of silk and patent American pumps; she had taken her to hydros. "But there she is!" bewailed the mother; "goin' on eight-and-twenty, and I'll swear she never had a box o' chocolates I didna buy for her mysel'! It's rale disheartenin', Mr Swan. I'd give a lot to see her settled down. But there! —ye'll think I'm just a sly designin' woman."

The traveller smiled. "So far as I can see," he said, "the trouble is that ye're no' half sly enough nor much o' a dab at the designin', or otherwise, if Rachel's like the world, you should hae been a granny. I've never seen her."

"Come up the stairs and ha'e a cup o' tea," said Mrs Thorpe; "I'm no' ashamed to let you see her."

"I will!" said Jimmy with alacrity, and gave a little twitch to his superb carnation.

If Rachel Thorpe was blate she showed no signs of it to him. He told her three quite funny stories, led the conversation on to operas, and sitting down to the piano vamped his own accompaniment (three good chords and a twiddly one) to "Star of Eve," which, he explained, was a good deal finer when sung by a tenor who could really sing. Rachel, thus encouraged, gave a palpitating rendering of "The Rosary," the widow looking all the time at Jimmy in expectant anguish as if he were an *entrepreneur* who was testing a soprano.

"Capital!" he murmured at the end of every verse. "Expression! Feeling! Temperament! Particularly that rallantando bit! For such a heavy song, she's simply wonderful!" He finally presented her with the carnation.

"Now, can you tell what's the matter wi' her?" asked the mother when she got him back into the shop. "Time's aye slippin' past, and a' the diffies in the place are gettin' married, and Rachel's jist the way ye see her."

"A bonny, wise-like lass!" said he, with emphasis. "Perhaps it wasna fair to call her Rachel. Rachel, Ruth, Rebecca —ony o' them's a handicap in this dull material age, Mrs Thorpe; ye want a snappy, cheery sort o' name to give a girl a chance. 'Rachel's solemn; it takes a lot o' pluck to put an arm about a Rachel. Ye should have ca'd her Jean. But she didna strike me as out o' the ordinar' shy; we got on together fine."

"Ah, yes," said Mrs Thorpe; "she got on a' right wi' you, for you're a married man, but if a lad comes to the house she hasna hardly got a word to say, and I've to do the talkin'."

"What do ye talk about to them?" asked Jimmy.

"Oh, anything at all," she answered, rather puzzled at the question. "Thank God, I never was at a loss for conversation! And Rachel, she sits fidgin'!"

"Yon's an interestin' photo album," said Jimmy, who had been personally conducted through it. "I suppose ye'll show them that?"

"Ye have to entertain them some way," said the widow sadly. "Especially if your daughter is a dummy."

"H'm!" said Jimmy, and rubbed his chin. "It's hardly fair to Rachel! There's half a dozen photos o' her yonder that amount to a complete exposure o' her past. 'Rachel as a baby' —nice, and wee, and fat; 'Rachel at the period o' the fringe,' 'Rachel when she won the ping-pong prize' — wi' a bolero jacketee, accordion pleats, and a motor kep. Ye shouldna rake up her past like that in front o' any chap ye're wantin' to encourage.

It mak's her look like the History o' Scotland in monthly parts."

"I never thought o' that!" said Mrs Thorpe.

"Besides, the album, as a whole, is obsolete as a social and domestic cheerer–up. It's done! Ye might as well attempt to rouse enthusiasm wi' a game o' dominoes or a spellin'-bee. Any young man that you show through yon album is bound to get a fright when he sees three generations o' the Thorpes and a' their ramifications down to sixty-second cousins. It reduces Rachel to a mere incident. He's apt to say to himsel', 'Great Scot! she's no unique at all: there have been hundreds o' her!' And it's so unlucky there's so mony o' them deid! Brief life is here our portion, as the hymn says, but we needna rub it in to Rachel's friends that even the Thorpes get old and disappear; they want to think of her as in eternal youth, for ever gaily skippin' across the sands o' time in a hobble skirt and clocked silk stockin's."

"Ye're a droll man!" said Mrs Thorpe laughing.

"And then there's another thing," said Jimmy twinkling. "I'll wager ye're far too anxious to be nice to any young man ye see in Rachel's company. That's no' the way to take the situation at all! My mother-in-law knew better than that when I was after Bella —that's the mistress. She forbade me to come near the house after her lassie, and used to look on me like dirt. She said the Swans were a' geese, and warned Bella to have naething to dae wi' me. Up till then Bella, wi' me, was just a lass for walkin' hame from the dancin' wi'; but when my pride was roused I up and married her! And the auld yin laughed!"

"That might do wi' others," said the widow, "but no wi' Rachel; she's so blate."

"Blate!" said Jimmy. "That'll be her salvation; there's far mair chance for a blate yin than the other kind. If she's really blate, and we had her down in Gleska she would be a novelty. Onything out o' the ordinar' takes in Gleska. Send her down for a week to Mrs Swan, to see the shops; there's nothing beats a change o' air for blateness."

"It's very kind o' ye," said Mrs Thorpe. "She wouldna be the worse for't, maybe. But ye'll think I'm an awfu' designin' woman!"

"Good!" said Jimmy heartily. "Bella will be glad to see her. And as for the designin', Mrs Thorpe. God meant it."

XVII

RACHEL COMES TO TOWN

James Swan had mischievously described the girl from Banchory to his wife as "a spindly one wi' ruby hair, a voice like the start o' a gramophone, and clothes picked up in the dark at a jumble sale," and when the visitor jumped out of a taxi-cab, which also bore a substantial trunk, a leather hat-box, a neat morocco dressing-case, and a bag of golf-clubs, from the railway station, Mrs Swan immediately realised that she had been badly done.

"I can't believe a word you say to me, sometimes, Jimmy!" she exclaimed with agitation, as the door bell rang.

There was nothing spindly about Rachel; her hair was a glorious golden; her voice was sweet and mellow as a mavis' song, and her dress alone was summed up in two seconds by Mrs Swan as costing anything over £6.10s.

"And where's the blateness of her?" Jimmy was asked at the earliest opportunity. "I thought from your description that you couldn't drag a word from her except in the dummy alphabet."

Jimmy chuckled. "I only told ye what her mother said," he answered. "The case is desperate. She's goin' on eight and twenty —"

"Just a child!" said his wife from the point of view of forty.

"Everybody in Banchory's gettin' married but hersel'; take her round the town before we go to Kirn, and give her wrinkles."

"The only kind of wrinkles I have nowadays are the sort a woman gets from being married," said Mrs Swan with a look at herself in the overmantel mirror.

But really Rachel Thorpe required no wrinkles. Jimmy was off the road for a week and busy at the warehouse; for three nights in succession, when he came home at tea-time, he found a vacant house and the fire out; a hitherto conscientious wife was being dragged around the town at the heels of the blate young thing from Banchory, and wasn't even ashamed of herself.

"I never go anywhere, James," she said; "you never take me over the door. I've seen more of Glasgow in the past three days with Rachel than I've done in twenty years with you."

The ladies together went to picture-palaces, tea-rooms, parks; they paraded Buchanan Street and Sauchiehall Street by the hour, fascinated by windows; they rode on the outside of tramway cars as far as cars would take them; one night they were not home till ten; Rachel had insisted on a music-hall.

"Oh, it's all right!" said Jimmy, meekly. "I'm vexed I never thought o' makin' ye a hot supper. I'll leave the door on the Chubb after this, and ye can jist slip in when ye like. There'll be something cold on the sideboard. But for goodness' sake don't start singin' and pullin' beer and make a row and wake me; mind, I'm gettin' up in years."

"You should come out with us," seriously suggested the girl from Banchory. "What's the sense of sitting in here moping all alone when you might be enjoying yourself? Mrs Swan and I are going to see "Way Back in Darkland' to-morrow night. I've just been telling her I hear it's fine."

"No," said he, ironically; "I canna be bothered goin' anywhere unless I can get dancin'; I'm vexed it's no' the social season; you and Bella would like a ball."

On his wife had come the most extraordinary transformation. The fashion in which she put up her hair was preposterously antiquated, according to Rachel, who dressed it to look three times as thick as it was before, with glints of sunshine in its bronze that no one had hitherto suspected. Rachel also in an hour or two devised a hat for Mrs Swan, so chic and saucy that of itself it immediately knocked ten years off her age, and induced in the wearer a corresponding spirit of youthful gaiety. She took about a breadth from the width of her Sunday gown, reduced its length amazingly, bought the nattiest kind of shiny shoes, and displayed in the frankest manner a beautiful pair of shot-silk stockings. Her husband saw her one day jump on a car with Rachel, and they looked like a couple of soubrettes in "The Girl in the Film."

"Ye seem to have picked me up a' wrang, Bella," he said to his wife when they were alone that evening. "The idea was that Rachel Thorpe was to have her shyness polished off wi' a week in Gleska, and maybe learn a tip or twa on the way to get a sweetheart. There's no' that mony sweethearts disengaged in Gleska that ye can look for one a-piece. Besides, as lang as I hing on, it wouldna be respectable."

"Pooh!" said Bella, radiantly; "you want to see me going out a perfect fright. I never had a fling to myself since I was married, and now that Rachel's here I'm going to have it. Your idea of what is fit and proper in a married woman's fifty years behind the times. Rachel was quite astonished at the life I lead."

"And that's the girl her mither thinks is blate!" said Mr Swan, derisively.

The Swans had taken three weeks of a house at Kirn; they removed to the coast on Monday, and the girl from Banchory went with them. In two days she had taught Mrs Swan the game of golf, how to swing most effectively in a hammock, the two-step, "Hitchy-Koo" and diverse other pleasing ditties, the right deportment for a walking-stick, and the way to clear the bows of a steamer by ten yards in a rowing-boat so as to get the rocking of the waves and a good view of the captain dancing with rage on the bridge.

Jimmy came down from town one afternoon, and saw them waiting for him on the pier. At first he had looked at them with amiable and even approving interest, for he did not, at a distance, recognise them. They had white serge skirts, white shoes and stockings, knitted sports-coats of a vivid mustard colour, knitted caps conform thereto in hue, and walking-sticks. They were distinctly making gallant play at coquetry with two young gentlemen he did not know, and to whom he was introduced with some embarrassment on the part of all concerned.

"There's just one thing ye have overlooked," he told his wife, who dropped behind with him while the blate girl from Banchory went up the pier between the two young gentlemen, putting down her feet with splendid artfulness so that nobody could help looking at them. Next to Mrs Swan's they were the neatest feet on the Cowal side of the coast that day.

"What do you mean? What did I overlook?" asked Mrs Swan, who seemed deliriously happy.

"The dug," said Jimmy, seriously. "Ye need a wee bit toy terrier under your oxter, and instead o' the walking-stick I would hae a tennis-racket. If I may ask, where did ye pick up thae twa misguided gentlemen?"

"Oh, just on the quay," said Mrs Swan. "They're very nice. They came off a boat from Rothesay."

"Did they just wink at ye, or did you see them first and say, 'Ha, Berty!'?"

"Nothing so common!" said Mrs Swan, with dignity. "We pretended we didn't see them, but they would insist on speaking to Rachel."

"Just that!" said Jimmy. "I'm goin' to write to Rachel's mother the night and tell her to get Rachel shifted back to Banchory as quick as possible, before my happy home is broken up."

His wife laughed. "Do you know who they are?" she said. "They're just two Banchory friends of Rachel's, and the one with the fancy waistcoat wants to marry her. He came here specially to ask her, and she says she will."

73

"Could he no' ask her up in Banchory?" asked Jimmy with surprise.

"No," said Mrs Swan; "not without her mother over-hearing. She was always there, and kept cracking Rachel up so much that the poor lad never got a chance to shove a word in telling his intentions."

"That's exactly what I thought!" said Mr Swan. "But what are you, at the age of over forty, comin' out so strong in the nutette line for?"

"Just to cheer up and encourage Rachel; just to make her think that married life's no' so dull as she would think if she saw me at my ordinary," said the amazing Mrs Swan.

XVIII

A POOR PROGRAMME

"You're the last landlord on this side of the Clyde to keep slippers for your guests," said Mr Swan. "It's not that I'm needin' them myself, but I like to see them; they're one of the few surviving relics of the age *de luxe* in the history of commercial travellin'."

"Do you know the way I manage to keep them, Mr Swan?" said the landlord of the Queen's. "I got them big! There's not a coffee-room pair of slippers here that's under easy number tens. It was a waiter, Alick Russell, put me up to't. I lost about a gross of slippers every year through gentlemen finding them so good a fit they thought they were their own. 'Whit ye want,' says Alick, 'is big and roomy yins they canna walk upstairs to their bedrooms wi'. I went away at once and bought three dozen pair of number tens. The only man they ever fitted was a cattleman from Perth. The rest just leave them."

Mr Swan put on his own slippers.

"You're surely not in for the night?" said Mr Grant; "there's a Territorial concert on."

Just for a moment Jimmy hesitated. "No," he said; "I'm bye wi' country concerts; they're too heatin' for my blood. If it was a swarry and a ball, or a Council meetin', I might risk it. That's the worst of bein' highly cultivated —I canna put up wi' 'Hitchy-Koo,' and they're bound to have 'Hitchy-Koo' in Fochabers, especially wi' a Territorial concert. It's a hundred chances to one a Colour-Sergeant wi' a nearly-tenor voice'll stand up and give 'The Phantom Army,' and as sure as daith I cannot stand 'The Phantom Army.' It was maybe good enough till the hundred thousandth time I heard it, but then it began to spoil my sleep. Forbye, 'The Phantom Army''s no' a song for Territorials; it's far too personal."

"They have a lot of talent," said the landlord coaxingly.

"I know they'll have," said Mr Swan agreeably. "I notice in the country papers that they're always super-excellent. Did it ever occur to you, Mr Grant, that music's done in Scotland? I mean vocal music; of course there's aye the pianola. There are only two kinds o' singers now in Scotland —the real professional that needs an evening suit for't, and the young and healthy amateur who does 'Phil the Fluter's Ball' or 'No, John, No!' as if his life depended on it."

"The gramophone —" said Mr Grant.

75

"Of course! Quite right! The gramophone's the music master now; whenever 'Everybody's Doing It' comes out in a Glasgow Pantomime, they wire at once from Fochabers to send a dozen records. No time is lost! The latest rag–time tune is up at Thurso wi' the mornin' post, and everybody's whistlin't by tea–time."

"Half the folk in the country's sick–tired o' music, and the other half's tryin' to be Clara Butts and Harry Lauders —a thing that sounds quite easy when you hear it in a canister. Half the nice wee lassies that could sing like laverocks if they were content to sing the way that God intended them, fair sicken ye wi' tryin' to get cadenzas like the banker's Tetrazzini, ten–and–six the double–breasted disc. The other half realise they could never do anything within a mile of it, and they never try; they just put up their hair another way, and tell the chap they're fond of cookin'."

"But still it's a very decent programme," said the landlord producing it.

Mr Swan put on his glasses. "That's it! I knew it at once!" he said. "'The Prologue from Pagliacci, by Mr G. R. Williamson.' I don't ken Mr Williamson, but I'll bet ye he's a tall, thin, fair–haired chap in the Union Bank, and has a lisp. He'll be at least a light and easy baritone: he couldn't do't unless. Then there's 'A Wee Deoch an' Doruis' —I ken that, too! He'll likely be a gas collector, a smart wee blackavised chap wi' a comic kind o' face and a crackle up aboot the F. Comic singing is sappin' the manhood o' the nation; it's worse than cigarettes. 'Angus Macdonald,' by Miss — Oh! take it away and put it in the larder! The only thing I see on the programme worth a rap is 'God save the King'; that's about the only chance that folk get now for singing.

"The place where people sing is Wales, and emulation o' the gramophone hasna spoiled them," said Mr Swan, warming to his subject. "Not being a solo vocalist myself, I always thought harmonic music was the best, and that's the notion o' the Welshmen. You see it gives a modest kind o' chap like me a chance. Thirty years ago there was some sense o' vocal music left in Scotland; there were choirs; now they think a choir is jist a special place for sittin' in the kirk. So long as there were choirs and glee parties there was some hope for us, though we maybe werena just exactly Covent Garden opera. We sang for singing's sake, and we didna try to beat the gramophone.

"There's two things worth while in this world —gettin' a Saturday to yoursel' and singin' bass in a choir that has a decent tenor. I never was happier! And music —genuine music —never got a better chance. So far as I'm aware there was never anything positively rotten put in harmony;

quartet, glee, and catch were always decent. Three-fourths of the agony of life to-day is due to that ridiculous preference for the solo. When the average amateur soloist comes in leanin' heavily on himself wi' a couple o' music sheets —one for the poor soul at the instrument and the other for himself to hide his presentation watch-chain —I'm sorry for him.

"I'm all for choirs and a good bass part for willing gentlemen! It's only wi' part-singing that ye'll stem the tide of British musical decadence — what do you think of that for rhetoric at this early hour o'evening, Mr Grant?"

"I like 'O, Who Will o'er the Downs?' and 'Kate Dalrymple,'" said Mr Grant with modesty.

"Right you are!" said Mr Swan emphatically. "Your tastes are sound! They werena tripe —these songs —at any rate!"

"All these remarks o' mine," continued Mr Swan, "are due to the fact that at a Glasgow public dinner the other night there was a choir. I havena heard a choir at a Glasgow public dinner for twenty years, and I'm thinkin' neither did the company. The usual idea o' a Glasgow dinner now is that a dozen men spoil a' the fun wi' makin' speeches. You'll never convince the poor deluded creatures that they have not something new to say, and that folk don't want to hear them. Nobody ever does. It just fair spoils the coffee and cigars.

"At this dinner some daring innovator introduced a choir, the speakin' was cut down to the assurance that the Navy was right and trade was boomin', and the choir took up the rest o' the evening makin' us really happy. If dinners were a' like that one, they would be my hobby."

"Then you're not coming?" said Mr Grant.

"Not me!" said Jimmy, lighting his pipe; "be sure and lock the door when ye come back. And tell the Pagliacci gentleman he hasna't in him! Tell him to start a decent choir."

77

XIX

BRODERICK'S SHOP

James Swan went into an Argyle Street shop on Saturday to buy a knife. It is one of the oldest ironmongery shops in town, but that was not the reason Jimmy went to it; antiquity of itself makes no appeal to him; he went to this particular shop because he knew the owner, who had for years been on the verge of losing money in it.

Elsewhere in Argyle Street it was the busiest hour of the day. All the world seemed out for buying. Drapery warehouses were crowded to the doors, the grocery shops, which also advertise, appeared too small for the folk who wanted into them; the lust for giving money in exchange for something crowded the street itself with gutter merchants feverishly dispensing fruit, and flowers, and penny toys that last (with care) till Monday. Argyle Street blazed with light and roared with commerce; electric moons, refulgent, made it bright as day; a thousand windows gorgeously displayed their best; the pavements streamed with life, and every other person had a parcel

"Beautiful!" said Jimmy to himself. "Tip-top! Lovely! And just to think that this was once a country lane!"

He felt a genuine pride in Glasgow, and a personal pride that he was an essential part in its commercial activities. It was with almost a paternal eye he stopped to look at a window with a dummy figure wearing one of C. & M.'s "Incomparable" Long-Busk Corsets, there because himself had thrown no little poetry into its recommendation.

To step from the street into Broderick's ironmongery shop, however, was to leave the roar of battle and get into a mausoleum. A solemn hush prevailed there. A customer was standing at the counter, plunged in the patient contemplation of long rows of rather dusty shelves with nothing more attractive to the eye on them than screw-nail packages. In parts behind two shopmen blew or flicked the dust from other packages; Broderick himself was on the ladder.

He came down at last, deliberately; gave a friendly nod to Jimmy; opened the parcel he had brought down with him, and found it was the wrong one. So he went up the ladder again, and in the course of time disposed of a key-ring to the customer for a penny. The customer gave sixpence for its payment. Mr Broderick picked the sixpence up and walked with dignity to some place far away in the back of his shop where he kept his cash-desk.

Jimmy took out his watch and held it in his hand.

The hum of the clamant, buying street came in, like some far murmur of a sea; below the wan, old-fashioned gas-light over Broderick's door ("Established 1812"), the multitude went skliffing past along the pavement, deigning not so much as a glance within. He hummed the funeral march from "Saul" to himself, and felt exceedingly sorry for Alick Broderick.

When Broderick had got the change for sixpence and dismissed his customer, he turned with a pathetic expansiveness to Jimmy.

"There's no' much profit aff a penny split ring, Jimmy," said he.

"I daresay no," said Jimmy, snapping up his hunter watch with a last glance at the dial. "Show me a shilling knife, and then shut up this shop o' yours, and come out and ha'e a dram."

"Indeed," said Broderick, "I might well shut it up for a' that's daein'. I never saw things worse"; and he took out a case of knives with great solemnity.

"Alick," said Mr Swan, "do ye mind the day ye blooded my nose in old Maclean's Academy?"

"Aye, fine!" said Mr Broderick. "Ye stole my jawry-bool."

"Weel, I'm gaun to blood your nose the night," said Jimmy, smiling. "Ye better get oot your hanky . . . .Ye say that things were never worse. Where are your ears and e'en? Take a daunder alang the street and hear things humming. I could hardly get alang the pavement for folk fair daft to spend their money, and here are you sclimbin' ladders and wearin' oot your shoon to get change for a customer that wants a penny ring. It took ye exactly one minute and forty-five seconds to go away back there to your cash-desk."

"For a' that's daein' —"started Mr Broderick.

"For a' that's daein' —fiddlesticks!" said Jimmy. "There's only six hundred minutes in a workin' day, and you have only the one pair o' legs on ye, and ye waste good minutes and good legs on the heid o' a penny ring. What ails ye at a cash railway, man? Or if ye canna hae a railway, can ye no' keep your cash beside your counter? Naebody's gaun to pinch it on ye! When a customer sees ye makin' a North Pole expedition awa' back there wi' his penny, he thinks he has paid too much for the ring, and ye're away behind to dance the hoolichan."

"There's naething to be done in business nooadays unless ye advertise," said Mr Broderick sadly; "and I never was in wi' advertisin'."

"Were ye no'?" said Jimmy, sharply. "What's your window for but advertisin'?"

"The cost's enormous," said Mr Broderick.

"Have ye ony money bye ye?" asked Jimmy, boldly.

"Thank God I have a little," said Mr Broderick.

"It would need to be a lot," said Jimmy, "for it's you that pays for other ironmongers' advertising, and nae thanks for it."

"I don't understand ye, Jimmy," said his friend. "How do I pay for other folks' advertisin'?"

"Who in heaven's name do ye think pays for't?" said Jimmy.

"The man that advertises."

"Not him! He doesna pay a penny. All he does is to lend a little capital in advertising, that comes back a hundred-fold. The more he advertises, the bigger his profits at the end of the year. When did ye ever hear o' a big advertiser failin'? The thing's unknown, and advertisin's only in its infancy."

"Aye, but in the long-run it's the customer that pays for advertisin'," said Mr Broderick.

"There, ye're wrang again!" said Jimmy. "What dae ye charge for this shilling knife?" and he picked up one that met his fancy.

"Just a shillin'," said Mr Broderick.

"Well, I can go to any ironmonger's shop in Gleska that advertises, and I'll get the same knife for a shillin'. Things are never ony dearer in a shop that advertises. So ye see it's neither the advertiser nor the customer that pays the newspapers."

"If it's no', wha is it, then?" asked Mr Broderick, with genuine interest. He had never studied the point before.

"It's you, and the like o' you!" said Jimmy. "Every customer you lose through no' advertisin', and every shop that goes doon through no' advertisin', swells the volume o' business in the shops that advertise, and indirectly pays for other folk's advertising. I never see your name in the papers, but when I read a splash o' Grant & Richards, I say to mysel', 'There's some more o' Alick Broderick's money!' . . . Take you my tip, Alick, blaw the stour aff them shelves and get a nice wee cash railway and ladder that runs on wheels, and hing oot some dacent lights, and advertise, and ye'll no' complain o' naething daein'."

He paid for his knife and gave a genial chuckle. "Now take out your hanky, lad!" he cried as he left the shop.

A hundred yards along the street he looked at a window of Grant & Richards, in whose shop a roaring trade was doing, and he saw a knife there priced at ninepence in every respect the counterpart of the one he had bought from Broderick.

"Stung!" he said to himself, with a humorous grin. "Alick's got the best o' me again, and it's me that needs the hanky."

XX

GENT'S ATTIRE

The utmost surprise was created last Friday in Campbell & Mcdonald's warehouse when Mr Swan appeared in a familiar overcoat. In the memory of the oldest employee he had never previously been known to inaugurate the winter season in any other coat than one quite unmistakably fresh from the tailor's hands. Nothing less would have seemed becoming and appropriate to the oldest traveller for the oldest soft goods firm in Glasgow. The tradition, long prevalent among the warehouse staff of C. & M., was that Jimmy Swan owed much of his renown and success as a traveller to the cut and fashion of his garments, always meticulously fresh and trim, and worn with a certain distinction which was the envy and despair of the younger travellers. They also tried to dress like gentlemen, but only partially succeeded, and always stuck at the half-way stage, where the best that can be said of a wearer of clothes is that he is a knut. They knew it themselves, when Jimmy's eyebrows would lift at the sight of their heliotrope wood-fibre sox or what they had fondly thought a stunning effect in waistcoats.

Yet here was Jimmy Swan in a last winter's greatcoat, ready to start on the northern journey through towns and villages to which, for years, he had been "the glass of fashion and the mould of form" —the seasonal inspiration and example of gent's styles as approved and passed in the Metropolis!

A lapse! A decided and disquieting lapse! It was inconceivable that the best shops in, say, Aberdeen, would give such orders as they used to do, to Jimmy Swan in a last year's topcoat, however cunningly cleaned and pressed to look like new.

"Excuse the liberty, Jimmy," said Carmichael the mantle-buyer, "but what's the matter wi' your tailor? Has your credit stopped?"

Mr Swan, puffing a little, rose from the case he was bent over, packing samples, and shrugged his shoulders.

"No," he answered. "If it's my coat you mean, it's just economy. Quite a good coat!"

"Ah! well," conceded Carmichael, "we have all to exercise some thrift or other these days."

"No' in the buyin' branch o' this establishment!" said Mr Swan; "Mr Macdonald's notions o' economy are concentrated in the meantime on the expenses o' the man who books the biggest orders for his firm, and —

not to put too fine a point on it —that's me!"

"Good heavens! they're no' surely beginnin' to scrimp you, Jimmy?" ejaculated Carmichael, genuinely shocked; it was understood in the shop that up to a pound a-day, Mr Swan's bill for expenses passed the cashier unquestioned; that it was an historical right, like Magna Charta.

Mr Swan only smiled sadly. "Economy's a droll thing, Alick," he remarked; "it's like them Zeppelin bombs, ye never ken where it'll licht, these days. Mr Macdonald has all of a sudden found oot that my buyin' a topcoat or a suit o' clothes noo and then from our country customers, involves us, someway, in the Corrupt Practices Act. At least, it's the best excuse he could think o' for knocking a bit aff my expenses."

Carmichael looked supprised. "What does it matter to him where ye buy your clothes?" he asked. "But I never dreamt ye bought any in the country."

"Many and many a time!" said Jimmy. "But nobody can cast up to me that I ever wore them!"

He shut down the lid of his case, and strapped it tightly.

"If ever you had been on the road sellin'," he said, when that was done, "you would understand yoursel' what's meant by my auld topcoat, and Macdonald's new economy. Some o' you chaps get into the buyin' branch wi' little or nae education to speak o' in human nature. A buyer's cock-o'-the-walk; he doesna even need to study to be civil to the folk he deals wi'; it's very different wi' the bagman. I've seen me buy a Hielan' cape I wouldna be dragged oot o' the Clyde by Geordie Geddes in, and wear it a couple o' days in Dornoch just to please a draper and tailor there I expected a thumpin' order frae."

"Great Scot!" said Carmichael, horrified at the very idea of Mr Swan in a Dornoch cape. "But do ye mean to say they passed the price o' a cape in your expenses?"

"No quite!" said Jimmy. "I sold it at a loss o' a pound when I got to Glasgow, and put the pound doon in my bill. This time last year old Macdonald himself would be the first to agree that it was a pound well spent on the Dornoch orders for fishermen's trousers I used to bring him. Do you know this, Carmichael? I one time went the length o' a suit o' kilts, complete even to the sporran! It was in Inverness, frae a customer that was awfu' namely for his kilts. But Mr Macdonald kicked at kilts; it cost me £2, 10s. to get rid o' them to a Hielandman that had a wee pub doon on the Broomielaw.

"It is the firmly rooted conviction o' the drapery trade in the rural districts o' Scotland that it's fit to tackle gent's attire," continued Mr Swan. "They get the designs and plans for spring lounge suits frae last year's 'Tailor and Cutter' newspaper; heave a web o' tweed at their cutter the first fine day he's aff the spree, tell him the only change this season's in lapels, remind him that cotton lining's nae langer bein' put in breeks, then press a lump o' chalk and a fret-saw onto his tremblin' hands, and order him to proceed.

"I've passed through the hands o' mair country cutters than any other man in Scotland. Ye never catch me wearin' onything but a genuine Glasgow suit, but for the sake o' business I've had to order suits in lots o' places no' the size o' Fochabers, where they put rabbit pouches in your jacket whether ye poach or no', and would palm off a waistcoat wi' sleeves on ye if ye werena watchin'. There's at least a score o' country clothiers in Scotland that expect me to buy a suit or a topcoat frae them every year; the goods is sometimes waitin' ready for me when I land; if there's any difference in the length o' my sleeve since last year, they're ready to tak' in a hem.

"What do I dae wi' the clothes? I sometimes put them into my sample case and sell them in the next wee toon I come to as a model garment fresh from London, goin' at a dead-snip bargain. Some o' them I get rid o' in the packin' shop at fifteen shillin's or a pound less than I paid for them; many a time I'm left wi' a Harris tweed the wife can only use for cuttin' up to go under a runner carpet. But up till now the firm has played fair horney, and seen I didna lose on my diplomatic stimulation o' the tailor trade in the turnip districts."

"It's not fair!" said Carmichael emphatically.

"It is not!" agreed the traveller. "Macdonald's kickin' aboot 30s. I honestly spent in pushin' business in Clachnacudden last October. I had aye to tak' a suit in Clachnacudden; Elshiner the draper seen to that. He had aye a range o' home-dyed, homespun tweeds for the local cattle show, and a cutter that took your measure a' wrang in Gaelic wi' a piece o' string. I've got suits frae Elshiner I could never sell onywhere at a third o' what they cost me; they were that roary, and that defiant o' every law o' the male anatomy.

"Last October, when Elshiner's cutter was passin' the string all over my manly form, and stoppin' to tak' a snuff each time that Elshiner put doon the Gaelic figures in a pass-book, I says, 'Whit profit do ye expect to mak' aff this suit, Mr Elshiner?'"

"'Thirty shillin's or thereabouts,' says he.

"Ah, well!' says I; 'don't bother makin' it; I'll pay the 30s. and we'll be a' square.'

"He took the thirty shillin's right enough, but his pride was touched, for he someway jaloused I didna appreciate his suits. And if ye believe me, he has never given me an order since! That's the way Macdonald's kickin'."

XXI

KEEPING UP WITH COCHRANE

It is a stimulating thing to see a fellow-creature socially climbing, and up to a certain point Mr James Swan was quite delighted with the progress of his customer Watty Cochrane. He had in a sense been the making of Watty. It was he, nine years ago, who put Watty on to the excellent opening there was for an up-to-date drapery shop in Lairg. He selected his first stock for him; got him a good credit from C. & M.; put him up to the art of window-dressing; and got him a wife with some sensible Glasgow notions of a mantua department.

"She's doin' fine," said Mr Cochrane, after eighteen months of married felicity. "She brought in last year £150 o' profit to the business, all out o' that bit room behind there, where I used to keep my lumber. She calls it an atelier, whatever that is; so far as I'm concerned she might call it a fusilier, so long's she draws in business the way she does in homespun costumes."

"The main thing is she's up to guarantee," said Jimmy Swan. "I knew Kate Jardine was the sort to make a 'happy fireside clime,' and 'that's the true pathos and sublime o' human life,' as Burns says."

"There's nothing pathetic about £150," said Cochrane; "it's nearly £3 a week. But when ye speak about a fireside climb, ye've hit the mark; Kate and me's started climbin', and I lie awake at nichts sometimes wondering what I'll reach to if I keep my health. What would ye say to Provost Walter Cochrane, eh?" And the draper rubbed his palms together.

The traveller looked at him with a critical eye. "'Well done!' I should say. 'Ye have fine shouthers for a chain, and the right sort o' chest for a door-knocker. But see and no' let your heid swell, Walter, or I'll be vexed I went and wasted Kate on ye!'"

After that, on every journey to the North he could see the climbing of Watty Cochrane. Mr Cochrane was made the Captain of the Golf Club, and immediately burst forth in knickerbocker suits. At the urgent solicitation of the citizens —at all events at the urgent solicitation of two of them, who were on his books —he went into the Town Council and became assured of undying local fame as the introducer of the ash-bin cleansing system. He talked more about ash-bins and destructors to Jimmy Swan on his visits than about the drapery business.

"How's the mistress?" Jimmy asked him sometimes; she was never to be seen.

"Up to the ears in the atelier," would Walter say with pride; "she's thrang on a weddin' job for Invershin."

"I hope," said Jimmy, "she's on the climb, too. There canna be much fun in sclimbin' if your wife's to stand at the foot a' the time and steady the ladder."

"I don't quite catch ye?" said Councillor Walter Cochrane, convenor of the Sanitary Committee.

"What I mean," said Jimmy, "is that if you're goin' to climb awa' up to the giddy heights o' social and civic eminence ye seem to have your mind set on, and leave her up to the ears in the atelier, which is just the French for workshop, I'll consider I did an ill turn by Kate Jardine when I put her in your road. So far as I can see, this climbin's a' in the interest o' Walter Cochrane. If ye go on the way ye're doing, she'll soon no' be able to look at ye except through a bit o' smoked gless, the same's ye were an eclipse. I thought it was a wife I got for ye, and no' a heid mantle-maker."

"Do you know what she made last year in the dressmakin'?" asked Councillor Cochrane.

"I don't know, and I don't care," said Jimmy bluntly. "I could get ye scores o' dressmakers just as good from Gleska, but no' another wife like Kate Jardine, and I'm feared ye're tryin' to smother her in selvedges."

On Mr Swan's next journey to Lairg he was just in time to participate in a chippy little dinner given to a select stag company at the Inn to celebrate Councillor Cochrane's elevation to the bench of Justices of the Peace. The dinner was the new J.P.'s. Councillor Cochrane was obviously becoming very fond of himself. He made three separate speeches in a newly-acquired throaty kind of voice, which he seemed to consider incumbent on a J.P. Several times he took occasion to allude to his last interview with the Lord-Lieutenant of the County.

"Who's he?" Jimmy took the opportunity of asking.

"The Duke, of course," said Councillor Cochrane.

"Which o' them?" asked Jimmy innocently. "I never can mind the names o' them unless I look up Orr's Penny Almanac."

"Sutherland," said the new J.P. "He's the Lord-Lieutenant o' the County, and makes all the J.P.'s. At least, the names are put before him, and he signs the Commissions."

"Plucky chap!" said Jimmy. "Some men would bolt at the desperate responsibility. Listening to ye, there, Walter, I couldna help bein' sorry there's no' a uniform for J.P.'s the same as for Lord-Lieutenants. That heid o' yours 'll never get a chance until ye get a helmet."

The new J.P. considered the occasion incomplete without having his portrait done in oils, and he imported from Aberdeen a fearless young artist, who in five or six days achieved a masterpiece six feet high, wherein Councillor Cochrane was brilliantly revealed as the sort of man who is in the habit of sitting in a frock-coat suit, irrelevantly but firmly grasping a roll of vellum.

The consequence was that when Mr Swan returned to Lairg in autumn in the commercial interest of C. & M., he found his customer had flitted to a grand new villa. The fact was intimated casually over a counter piled with Jimmy's samples.

"Keep it up!" said Jimmy with an air of resignation. "Lairg's gettin' ower small for ye. And how is she gettin' on, hersel', in the atelier?"

"Thronger than ever!" said Councillor Cochrane, triumphantly. "Workin' till all hours since the shootin' started."

"Puir Kate!" said Jimmy. "She used to be the cheery yin when I kent her in Gleska. She used to hae her evenin's to hersel', and nae bother aboot a villa. What put the villa in your heid, Walter?"

"It was," said Councillor Cochrane, "the portrait to begin wi'. You see, in the old house the portrait was so big in the wee parlour it fair drowned everything else. Besides, in my position —" and he closed abruptly with a gesture which plainly indicated that the position of a J.P. with the prospects of further civic dignities demanded a reasonable area of domestic space to move about in. "What I want ye to do for me, now," he proceeded, "is to send me up from the Clyde a flag-pole for the front o' the house."

"What do ye want wi' a flag-pole?" said Jimmy with surprise. "Are ye goin' to start sclimbin' flag-poles next?"

"No," said Councillor Cochrane: "but a bit of a pole goes well wi' a villa. I see a lot o' them in the villas down at Inverness. Many a time a body wants to hoist a flag. A flag-pole gives a kind o' finish."

The flag-pole was duly ordered by Mr Swan, who had dreams of a greatly inflated Cochrane painfully sprawling up and sitting on the truck with Kate Jardine sitting making costumes at the foot. For months he had no communication with his soaring customer, but at last he got a letter asking him to keep his eye about for a couple of iron cannons, second-hand. The letter came to Jimmy one morning as he sat at home at breakfast, and he groaned as he perused it.

"What's the matter, Jimmy?" asked his wife.

"It's Watty Cochrane in Lairg," he told her. "He's goin' to shoot himsel', and he thinks himsel' that big it needs a couple o' cannons to do the job."

"Nonsense!" said Mrs Swan.

"No, I'm wrang!" said Jimmy, hastily, proceeding further with his reading of the letter. "They're for the front of the villa; he wants them four feet lang and mounted for he's noo a Bailie. I'll see him to the mischief first! I've troked aboot for mony a droll thing for my customers, but I draw the line at cannons. What'll he be wantin' next if they mak' him Provost?"

Jimmy went up to Lairg on his next North journey with a plausible tale that there was a positive dearth of second-hand cannons in the West of Scotland, as they were all taken up by the Territorial artillery.

"It doesna matter," said Bailie Cochrane, looking slightly worried. "I thought they would make a kind of artistic finish to the villa, but I doubt I'll have to do without them. What I'm wantin' more's a forewoman. You would hear the news?"

"No," said Jimmy.

"The wife's given up the atelier. . . It's twins," said Bailie Cochrane.

XXII

THE HEN CRUSADE

"Do ye mind yon hen ye were good enough to send my wife for her stall at the Bazaar?" asked Boyd the draper as Mr Swan was putting back his samples in their cases.

"Fine!" said Jimmy. "I hope it was all right?"

"It was right enough," said Mr Boyd, solemnly; "but it caused a lot o' ill-will among the customers," and Jimmy, bent above his cases, indulged in a crafty wink to himself.

"There wasn't a body came to that Bazaar," went on the draper, "that didn't want to buy the hen. There was what I might call a regular furore about her. And because one hen couldna be sold to four hundred different folk, they took the pet and went away without buyin' anything. I canna understand it; the folk in this place seem to be daft for poultry . . . What are ye laughing at, Mr Swan?"

"Was the Bazaar a success?" asked Jimmy.

"Indeed and it was not! They didna get half the money that they wanted, and I'm no' vexed; it wasna wi' my will that my wife gave countenance to a Bazaar to buy an organ; what we're needin's no' an organ, but a new minister; we're all fair sick o' Cameron . . . But what in a' the earth are ye grinnin' at, Mr Swan?"

"I'll tell ye that," said Jimmy; "I'm laughing at the continued triumph o' my Hen Crusade. You see, I'm utterly against Bazaars, Mr Boyd. They're the worst form o' Sweatin' that we have in this country. They're blackleg labour. They're bad for the shopkeeper's business, and they're bad for my firm, C. & M. If the craze for Bazaars went any further, I would soon be sellin' naething else but remnants, and folk would expect to get them gratis wi' a bonus ticket. Now, when a customer like yoursel' asks me for a trifle for his wife's stall, I darena well refuse; but I took a survey of the situation some time since, and I saw how I could please my customer and at the same time put a spoke in the Bazaar. The common hen, Mr Boyd, humble, unostentatious, and industrious in life, becomes, when dead, the valued friend o' British commerce."

"Yours was the only fowl in that Bazaar," said Mr Boyd, "and it fair upset it!"

"Exactly!" said Jimmy, rubbing his hands with the greatest satisfaction. "Works like a charm, every time! I'm strongly advising C. & M. to send a hen to every Bazaar that opens."

"Every person who came into that Bazaar made a dash at once for the produce stall and grabbed the hen, though it had a ticket 'Sold' on it before the door was opened."

"The wife, I suppose?" said Jimmy, innocently.

"Yes," said Mr Boyd, a little flushed. "It was a tidy hen; well worth the half-crown you put on it."

"I always fix the price as low as that," said Jimmy, though that hen cost me exactly three-and-nine. If the price is low, the competition is the keener."

"At last my wife had to send the fowl home before it was torn to bits by exasperated customers; but all the same everybody coming into that place till the latest hour at night was asking for the hen. And because we didn't have table-loads o' half-croon hens they took the huff and went away, as I say, without buyin' anything. The funny thing is they all kent there was a hen before they came near the place."

"They always do!" said Jimmy. "The rumour of something really useful in a Bazaar goes round a town like this like a fiery cross, and that's the phenomenon I take advantage of in my Hen Crusade. You see, it has got this length wi' Bazaars that they're filled wi' fancy-work no rational mortal soul could fancy. The first thing a woman does in the way o' contributin' to a stall is to cut up something useful and turn it into something ornamental, and the poor misguided body who buys it and brings it home is chaffed a lot about it by her husband. Then, in addition, there's at all Bazaars, a great bulk o' stuff that's never meant for either use or ornament —it's just Bazaar stuff, made for sellin'. The buyer takes it home and puts it out o' sight till the next Bazaar comes on, and makes it her contribution. It goes from Bazaar to Bazaar till it drops in pieces, or till folk canna guess what it was first intended for.

"It's some years now since the hen came to me as an inspiration. There's something about a hen wi' its heid thrawed that strongly appeals to human nature. I thought to mysel' if I can introduce one fair good hen at a temptin' price to a Bazaar, the struggle for its possession will kill that interest in fancy-work that's far better bought from the retail shops that buy from C. & M. It's sure to be bought at the very start by the lady who has it in her stall, and that in itself's annoyin' to the other customers. But, further than that, it's well enough known to every woman who goes about Bazaars that the only thing she can bring home from them to please her man is something he can eat. He has no use for home-made toffee, and he wouldna thank her for the minister's wife's conception o' a seed-cake. A fowl, on the other hand, will never go wrong wi' him, and that's the way ye'll notice that the rumour o' a hen for sale at a Bazaar brings up a queue o' women at the doors an hour before they're open. Half o' them have explicit orders from their husbands to buy that hen, and the other half are planning to give him a nice surprise.

"When the crowd find that the hen's awa' wi't already at half–a–crown to the lady at the stall, it goes home indignant without a glance at the table–centres, and that's another Bazaar burst! I'm tellin' you, Mr Boyd, it's aye weel worth a draper's while to make his contribution to a kirk Bazaar a sonsy hen marked down to a price that's temptin'. I've tried jucks, but jucks are no use; the public's dubious about jucks; ye can only rouse the spirit o' competition wi' a hen."

"You're an awfu' sly man, Mr Swan!" exclaimed the draper. "But I'm no vexed yon hen o' yours played havoc wi' the last Bazaar. I've quarrelled wi' the minister about that very organ, and now I havena any kirk to go to."

"It's surely no' for the want o' kirks," said Jimmy. "How many are there here for less than a thousand souls?"

"Five," said Mr Boyd sadly; "the Parish, the U.F., which I belong to, the Episcopalian that belongs to Mr Snodgrass of Blairmaddy, and two different kinds o' Frees, the Wee Frees and the —"

"Oh! never mind goin' into that," said Jimmy, "just say assorted. I never could tell the difference o' one Free Kirk from another, and I've studied the thing minutely, even to the way they cut their hair. A customer up in Ullapool tells me it's a' in the way ye carry your hat in your hand goin' up the aisle; if ye happen to carry it upside down you're seen to be a slider, and they fence the tables against ye at the next Communion, so ye have to join the other body."

"The worst of it with me,," said Mr Boyd, "is that there's no' another body in the town I could take up wi' and respect myself. But I'm done wi' Cameron! He wants an organ and a lectern. It would suit him better if he stuck to the fundamentals."

"What exactly's that?" asked Jimmy gravely, fastening a strap.

Mr Boyd was content to wave his hands in the manner which indicates that words are quite inadequate to express ideas. "It's a bonny-like thing," said he, "that I have to go to Glasgow for Communion Sunday! I certainly will not go to the table under Cameron! Could you recommend a sound U.F. in Glasgow, Mr Swan? I'll take my wife and family"

"Cameron?" said Jimmy, turning something over in his mind "The best kirk I can recommend's my ain, though ye'll have to thole the organ."

"I don't care!" said Mr Boyd, as he took a note of it. "Anything at all to get awa' from Cameron!"

Two weeks later all the family of Boyd came back from Glasgow looking rather drowned. They had been in the Communion.

"What way did ye get on?" a customer asked the draper on the day that followed their return.

"I didna get on at all!" said Mr Boyd disgustedly. "A fair take-in! It cost us £2, IOS. to go the week-end to Glasgow, and we a' went to the kirk that Swan the traveller recommended. There we were sittin' expectin' a rousin' sermon from the Rev. Walter Spiers, and sure o' havin' the fundamentals. When the bell stopped ringin', I heard a skliff o' feet from the vestry that struck me as familiar, and when I looked up to see who the beadle was snibbin' in the pulpit, who was this but Cameron!"

XXIII

LINOLEUM

Mr James Swan has lived for fifteen years in Ibrox. For the first six months he thought it horrible, and ever since he has vexed himself to think how foolish he was not to have gone there sooner. That is life. Men are like pot plants. You shift a geranium into a new pot, and for weeks it wilts, disconsolate, till some fine sunny day it seems to realise that other geraniums seem happy enough in the same sort of pots, and that it isn't the pot that matters really. Whereupon the geranium (which is actually a pelargonium) strikes fresh roots into the soil, spreads out a broader leaf, throws out a couple of blossoms, and delights in making the best of it. It takes the first prize at the local flower show; content in the best fertiliser. Jimmy Swan, after fifteen years in Ibrox, thinks Ibrox is the centre of the solar system. Take him to Langside or Partickhill, and he feels chilly; at Dennistoun he feels himself a foreigner, and looks at passing tramcars for the Southside as an exile from Scotland, haunting the quays of Melbourne, looks at ships from the Clyde with the names of Denny or Fairfield on their brasses. Jimmy said to me the other day, "I canna think how people can live ony where else than Ibrox. It's the best place in the world." "How?" I asked. "Well," said he, "it's-it's-it's-it's Ibrox!" A little inconclusive, but I quite understood. Nine-tenths of us have our Ibrox; the people to be sympathised with are those who haven't.

But Jimmy got an awful start the other day! He came home from the North journey on a Saturday very tired, and exceedingly glad to see the familiar streets of Ibrox again. Nothing had changed; the same ham was in the grocery window, apparently only a slice the less, and he had exactly the high tea he expected, but his wife was different. She plainly nursed some secret discontent. Quite nice, and interested in his journey, and all that, but still —

It turned out to be the linoleum. The lobby linoleum. She put it to Jimmy if a lobby linoleum seven years old could honestly be regarded as quite decent.

"Tuts! there's naething wrang wi' the linoleum," said her husband. "As nice a linoleum as anybody need ask for; I never tripped on't yet."

"The pattern's worn off half of it," said his wife; "Mrs Grant was in to-day, and I was black affronted. In her new house in Sibbald Terrace they have Persia rugs."

"Kirkcaldy's good enough for us," said Jimmy; "just you wait for a year or twa and ye'll see the fine new linoleum I'll get ye."

It was then that the shock came. Mrs Swan, having brooded for a while on the remoteness of a new linoleum, intimated with a calm that was almost inhuman that she had been looking at some houses to let in Sibbald Terrace. Their present house was become impossible any longer. It had all the vices conceivable in any house built of human hands, and several others peculiar to itself, and evidently of their nature demoniac. It was cold, it was draughty, it was damp, it was dismal. Its chimneys did not draw properly; its doors were in the wrong places; its kitchen range was a heartbreak; its presses were inadequate, —she took ten minutes to expose all its inherent defects as a dwelling, and left her astonished listener in the feeling that he had been living for fifteen years in an orange-box without knowing it.

"We'll have to flit!" she said at last, determinedly.

"Sibbald Terrace is no' in Ibrox!" said her husband, astonished at her apparent overlook of this vital consideration.

"All the better o' that!" said the amazing woman. "I'm sick o' Ibrox! You can say what you like, James Swan; I'll no' stay another year in this hoose."

"Ye're fair fagged oot, Bella," said her husband, compassionately. "I doubt ye have been washin', efter all I told ye. Ye should stay in your bed the morn, and never mind the kirk. Sick o' Ibrox? Ye shouldna say things like that even in fun!"

It was at this stage, or a few days after it, I met Mr Swan. He was chuckling broadly to himself. "Did you ever flit," he asked me.

"Once," I said.

"That's enough for a lifetime," said he. "Men would never flit any mair than they would change their sox if it wasna for their wives. The advantage o' an auld hoose is that ye aye ken where your pipe is. My wife took a great fancy to flit the other day, and I said it was a' right; that I would look oot for a new house. At the end o' three days I said I had a fair clinker —vestibule wi' cathedral glass in the doors, oriel windows in the parlour, fifteen by eight lobby, venetian blinds, bathroom h. and c., wash-hand basin, electric light, tiled close, and only five stairs up.

"She says, 'Do ye think I'm daft? Five stairs! Is it in the Municipal Buildin's?'

"'No,' says I; 'it's in Dalwhinnie Street.'

"'Where in a' the earth is Dalwhinnie Street?' says she.

"'It's a new street,' I said, 'near Ruchill. Ye take the car from aboot the foot o' Mitchell Street, come off at an apothecary's shop, and take the first turn to the right and ask a message-boy.'

"'I'll not go to any such street, James Swan!' she says; 'I would rather take a place!' and the dear lass was a' trimblin' wi' agitation."

"No wonder, Mr Swan," I said. "It sounded a very out-of-the-way locality. Where is Dalwhinnie Street?"

"There's no such street," said Mr Swan: "at least if there is, I never heard o't. But ye see I wanted to put her aff the notion o' flittin'. And there was Bella, almost greetin'! I let on I was fair set on Dalwhinnie Street because it was so handy for the Northern Merchants' Social Club. But Dalwhinnie Street, right or wrong, she would not hear tell o', and I said I would take another look round."

Mr Swan cocked his head a little and looked slyly at me. "Ye're a married man, yoursel'," said he. "Ye know what wives are. They're no' such intellectual giants as we are, thank God! or else they would find us oot; but once they've set their minds on a thing, Napoleon himself couldna shift them. Some days after that I cam' hame from Renfrewshire wi' a great scheme for takin' a house in the country. I said I had seen the very house for us —half-way between Houston and Bridge-of-Weir.

"'Whereabouts is Houston?' says the mistress in frigid tones, as they say in the novels.

"'It's half-way between the Caledonian and G. and S.W. lines,' says I, 'and if ye're in a hurry ye take a 'bus if it's there.'

"'What sort o' house is it?' she asked, turnin' the heel o' a stockin' as fast as lightning.

"'Tip-top!' I says. 'Nine rooms and a kitchen; fine flagged floor in the kitchen; spring water frae the pump in the garden; two-stall stable. Any amount o' room for hens; ye can keep hunders o' hens. The grocer's van passes the door every Thursday.'

"She began to greet. 'That's right!' she says. 'Put me awa' in the wilds among hens, so that I'll die, and ye'll can marry a young yin. But mind you this, James Swan; I'll no' shift a step oot o' Ibrox!'

"'Tuts, Bella!' I says, 'ye canna stay ony langer in this house; it's a' wrang thegither.'

"'There's naething wrang wi' the hoose,' says she, 'if I had jist some fresh linoleum.'

"'Well, well,' says I; 'ye'll get the linoleum' —and I was much relieved. 'I'll buy't tomorrow.' And I did. It cost me 4s. 6d. a yard.

"Your wife is a very clever lady, Mr Swan," I said; "she probably never thought of flitting, but badly wanted that linoleum."

"Of course!" said Jimmy Swan. "I kent that a' alang! But ye've got to compromise!"

XXIV

THE GRAUVAT KING

Most people —even in the the dry-goods trade —think that the Muffler that made Mildrynie Famous, and that great woollen factory which gives employment to thousands of people in Mildrynie, and has in ten years made a fortune for the Drummonds, owed their conception wholly to Peter Drummond. A great mistake! Peter Drummond, of himself, never had any imagination, initiative, or enterprise; till this day (between ourselves) he is a pretty poor fly, and his great national reputation as the Muffler King, his grand Deeside estate, his suberb collection of Old Masters, his deputy-lieutenantship, and the marriage of his daughter Cissy to Lord "Tivitty" Beauchamp, are due under Providence to Mr James Swan, traveller for the Glasgow firm of Campbell & Macdonald. There is a marble timepiece of the most ponderous and depressing character in Mr Swan's parlour, with an inscription on it which marks an epoch in the history of industrial Scotland. It says —

To JAMES SWAN, Esq.,

FROM

HIS FAITHFUL FRIEND,

PETER DRUMMOND

3 *JUNE* 1903.

———

"Lest we forget."

The clock doesn't go; it hasn't gone for years; it is merely a domestic monument —of ingratitude.

Peter Drummond, in 1903, was a customer of Jimmy Swan's in Mildrynie. He and his brother Alick (now Alexander Lloyd Drummond, Esq. of Ballochmawn) had a tiny draper's shop in East Street, next door to a smiddy which seemed to do nothing else from one end of the year till the other but singe sheep's heads for the inhabitants of Mildrynie, who at that time numbered eight hundred souls and two policemen.

One day Jimmy Swan turned up at the door with his sample cases, and found the brothers much depressed. They were doing wretched business. Their shop was off the main street; the propinquity of the smiddy and its perpetual odour of singed wool made the shopping public avoid it; things were come to such a pass that the Drummonds were contemplating closing up and going off to Canada.

"There's naething to be done in this hole o' a place," said Peter, who spoke Scotch in these days.

"There's plenty to be done in ony place if you're the kind o' man to do it," said Jimmy. "Mildrynie's no' much size; I've seen it missed a'thegither oot o' the maps; but for a' that it's a wonderful place, for it's fair in the middle o' the world. If it's a hole, as ye say, it's a hole to be respected, for it's like a hole in the middle o' a grindstane."

"Nonsense!" said Peter Drummond. "Aff the railway line, away up here in the North; it's oot o' the world a'thegither."

"Fair in the middle!" insisted Mr Swan. "Look you at a globe or a map o' the world, and ye'll see I'm richt. Every other place in the world's grouped roond aboot Mildrynie, just the same as if God had meant it to be great."

"Maybe that's so!" conceded Mr Drummond on reflection; "but my shop's no' in the middle o' Mildrynie, and so I whiles think I micht as weel ha'e my signboard up at the North Pole. That's the middle o' the world too,"

"What do ye dae to attract customers?" asked Jimmy, adjusting his carnation.

"Just what everybody else does that keeps a shop," said Peter Drummond.

"Error No. 1," said Jimmy. "The way to attract customers is to dae what naebody else is daein'. That's where the profit as well as the fun comes in. I would get sick-tired daein' the same as everybody else; the only excuse ye have for bein' alive is that ye dae some things peculiarly in your own way."

"I carry a good stock, and I show everything at a reasonable price," said Peter Drummond.

"Error No. 2," said Jimmy, blandly. "Ye should start sellin' something at a quite unreasonable price."

"What dae ye mean?" asked Mr Drummond.

"Sell it at what it costs ye. Here's a new line I have in woollen mufflers, as cosy as a fur-lined coat, and fastens wi' a snap. They'll cost ye half-a-croon each from C. & M., and that's even cootin' aff the discoont. The winter's comin' on; you make a splash wi' the Mildrynie Muffler at half-a-croon, and ye'll get the folk to your shop, for naebody else sells them for less than three shillings. Once ye have the folk buying your mufflers at cost price, it'll be gey droll if ye canna sell them other things at a reasonable profit."

"There's something in't!" said Peter Drummond.

On the next journey Mr Swan made to Mildrynie, he found that the half-crown muffler had moved the business slightly, but not enough to lift the spirits of the brothers Drummond. Their unpopular location and the smell of the smiddy were against a really popular and fashionable success.

"Do ye advertise?" asked Jimmy.

"No," said Peter; "naebody advertises here."

"My goodness! that's the very chance for you then!" exclaimed Mr Swan eagerly. "Chip in first before the others think o't. Advertise in the county paper —'The Real and Original Midrynie Muffler'; ye'll sell them like Forfar Rock!"

"But if naebody's wantin' mufflers?" said Peter, sadly.

"Naebody was wantin' Beecham's pills a hundred years ago, and noo they canna dae withoot them. Look at the way that soap's come into fashion, even in the country districts —a' the result o' advertisin'."

"It's the smell o' the smiddy next door that spoils this street," said Mr Drummond.

"Error No. 4642!" said Jimmy. "The smiddy 'll be a godsend if ye'll dae what I'm gaun to tell ye. Put you this advertisement in the local paper" — and he quickly drafted it out on a sheet of wrapping-paper —

THE MARVELLOUS MILDRYNIE MUFFLER

ONLY HALF-A-CROWN

DRUMMOND'S SHOP, 3 EAST STREET.

Follow your Nose and the Smell of Sheep's Head Singeing.

"I never saw an advertisement like that in a' my life," said Peter Drummond.

"Exactly!" said Jimmy. "That's the sort o' advertisement to advertise when ye're advertisin'."

On his next journey he found the Drummond business booming, and got an incredibly large order for Mildrynie mufflers at a price that left a reasonable profit for the retailer. But Peter was still a little depressed.

"There's money in't sure enough," said he; "but they ca' me the Grauvat King, and I don't like it."

"Nonsense!" said Jimmy. "It's just as fine to be the Grauvat King as the Oil King, or the Diamond King, or the Cattle King; it's a' the same to you so lang's ye get them on the neck. If you're the Grauvat King in Forfarshire, it's a' the easier for ye to be Muffler Monarch to the country at large. The Mildrynie Muffler's good enough to stand pushing just as far as Hielan' Whisky; you get a pickle money thegither and advertise the Rale and Original Mildrynie Half-croon Muffler in a' the papers in the country, and ye'll mak' a fortune. Tell them the Mildrynie Muffler's made aff pure hygienic wool that's grown on high-pedigree Hielan' sheep that graze on the heathery slopes o' the Grampian Mountains, the land where the eagle soars and the cataract flashes; that it's manufactured in the cottage homes o' the God-fearin', clean, and industrious native peasantry, and is recognised by the faculty as the one garment responsible for the sturdy health and universal longevity o' the Scottish race, and C. & M. 'll keep ye supplied wi' a' ye want; there's plenty o' mills in bonny wee Gleska."

It was in recognition of this valuable tip that Peter Drummond, a twelvemonth later, gave Mr Swan the time-piece —a poor solatium to Mr Swan for his loss of Drummonds' muffler trade when they opened the enormous works of their own at Mildrynie.

XXV

JIMMY'S SINS FIND HIM OUT

Mr James Swan picked up a bunch of violets, which he had been refreshing in a tumbler while he wrote out his expenses for the week, and placed it in his button-hole. From a pocket he took a small case-comb, and, borrowing from Pratt, the office "knut," the little mirror which Pratt kept always in his desk to consult as often as the Ready Reckoner, he went to the window and combed his hair.

"Which side are sheds worn on this season?" he asked Pratt, whom it was the joke of the office to treat with mock deference as arbiter of fashion, expert, and authority upon every giddy new twirl of the world of elegance.

"To the left," said Pratt, without a moment's hesitation, and with the utmost solemnity; the parting of his own hair was notoriously a matter of prayerful consideration. He was a lank lad with a long neck; it looked as if his Adam's apple was a green one and was shining through —a verdant phenomenon due to the fact that he had used the same brass stud for three years.

"Can't be done on the left," said Mr Swan. "That's the side I do my thinkin' on, and it's worn quite thin. I envy ye your head o' hair, Pratt; it'll last ye a lifetime, no' like mine."

Pratt, with the mirror restored to him, put it back in his desk with a final glance at it to see that his necktie was as perfectly knotted as it was three minutes ago; put on his hat and bolted from the office.

"They're a' in a great hurry to be off the day," said Mr Swan to himself. "I wonder what they're up to?"

He was to find out in two minutes, to his own discomfiture.

At the foot of the stair which led to the upper warehouse he ran against Peter Grant of Aberdeen, who was in search of him.

"My Jove!" said Grant, panting; "I'm in luck! I was sure ye would be awa' to't, and I ran doon the street like to break my legs."

"De-lighted to see ye, Mr Grant!" said Jimmy with a radiant visage. "This is indeed a pleasant surprise! But ye don't mean to tell me ye came from Aberdeen this mornin'?"

"Left at a quarter to seven," said Grant. "I made up my mind last night to come and see it. And I says to mysel', 'If I can just catch Mr Swan before he goes to the field, the thing's velvet!' "

"De-lighted!" said Jimmy, and shook his hand again. But the feeling of icy despair in his breast was enough to wilt his violets.

His sin had found him out! There was only one inference to be drawn from Peter Grant's excited appearance; he had carried out the threat of a dozen years to come and see a Glasgow football match, and expected the expert company and guidance of C. & M.'s commercial traveller.

And Jimmy Swan had, so far as Grant was concerned, a reputation for football knowledge and enthusiasm it was impossible to justify in Glasgow, however plausible they seemed in a shop in Aberdeen. Grant, who had never seen a football match in his life, was a fanatic in his devotion to a game which for twenty years he followed in the newspapers. Jimmy in his first journeys to Aberdeen had discovered this fancy of his customer, and played up to it craftily with the aid of the "Scottish Referee," which he bought on each journey North for no other purpose, since he himself had never seen a football match since the last cap of Harry M'Neill of the "Queen's," in 1881.

The appalling ignorance of Jimmy regarding modern football, and his blank indifference to the same, were never suspected by his customer, who from the traveller's breezy and familiar comments upon matches scrappily read about an hour before, credited him with knowing all there was to know about the national pastime.

When Jimmy was in doubt about the next move in a conversation with Grant, he always mentioned Quinn, and called him "good old Jimmy." He let it be understood that the Saturday afternoons when he couldn't get to Ibrox were unhappy —which was perfectly true, since he lived in Ibrox, though the Rangers' park was a place he never went near.

"I'll go and see a match some day!" Grant always said; he had said it for many years, and Jimmy always said, "Mind and let me know when ye're comin', and I'll show ye fitba'."

And now he was taken at his word!

What particular match could Grant have come for? Jimmy had lost sight of football, even in the papers, for the past three months.

With an inward sigh for a dinner spoiled at home, he took his customer to a restaurant for lunch.

"I want to see M'Menemy," said Grant; "it was that that brought me; he's a clinker!"

"And he never was in better form," said Jimmy. "Playin' like a book! He says to me last Monday, 'We'll walk over them the same's we had a brass band in front of us, Mr Swan!' "

"Will they win, do ye think?" Grant asked with great anxiety; he was so keen, the lunch was thrown away on him.

"Win!" said Jimmy. "Hands down! The—the—the other chaps is shakin' in their shoes."

So far he moved in darkness. Who M'Menemy was, and what match he was playing in that day, he had not the faintest idea, and he played for safety. It was probably some important match. The state of the street as they had walked along to the restaurant suggested a great influx of young men visitors; it might be something at Celtic Park.

He looked at Grant's square-topped hat and had an inspiration.

"If ye'll take my advice, Mr Grant," said he, "ye'll go and buy a kep. A hat like that's no use at a Gleska fitba' match; ye need a hooker. If ye wear a square-topped hat it jist provokes them. I'm gaun round to the warehouse to change my ain hat for a bunnet; I'll leave ye in a hat shop on the road and then I'll jine ye."

"What fitba' match is on the day?" Jimmy asked a porter in the warehouse.

"Good Goad!" said the porter with amazement at him; "it's the International against England."

"Where is it played?" asked Jimmy.

"Hampden, of course!"

"What way do ye get to't, and when does it start?"

"Red car to Mount Florida; game starts at three; I wish to goodness I could get to't," said the porter

Jimmy looked his watch. It was half-past one.

He found Grant with a headgear appropriate to the occasion, and wasted twenty minutes in depositing his hat at Buchanan Street left-luggage office. Another twenty minutes passed at the station bar, where Jimmy now discoursed with confidence on Scotland's chances, having bought an evening paper.

"Will ye no' need to hurry oot to the park?" Grant asked with some anxiety. "There'll be an awfu' crood; twenty chaps wi' bunnets came on at Steenhive."

"Lot's of time!" said Jimmy with assurance. "We'll tak' a car. Come awa', and I'll show ye a picture palace."

It was fifteen mintutes to three when they got to Hampden. A boiling mass of frantic people clamoured round the gates, which were shut against all further entrance, to the inner joy of Mr Swan, who lost his friend in the crowd and failed to find him.

"Where on earth were you till this time?" asked his wife when he got home to Ibrox two hours later.

"Out in the Queen's Park," said Jimmy truthfully. "Wi' luck I lost a man outside a fitba' match, and spent an hour in Camphill —no' a soul in't but mysel' —listenin' to the birds whistlin'."

XXVI

A WAVE OF TEMPERANCE

One day last week an hotel in Falkirk had six commercial travellers from Glasgow in its commercial room at dinner, the president and *doyen* of them Jimmy Swan, who unfeelingly depressed the company by drinking ginger ale. It was not so much his choice of this unorthodox beverage that saddened them as his evident enjoyment of it; he lingered over it, and smacked his lips upon it, and cocked his eye to look through the bubbling glass as if it were Clicquot, 1904. The others suddenly realised that this ostentatious gusto carried some reproach on their preferance for bitter beer —so they defiantly ordered in another pewter each.

"You should try sour milk, Mr Swan," said that hardened satirist, Joe M'Guire, the boot man; "it's said to be full o' the finest germs. If you drink sour dook you'll live to the age o' a hundred and fifty, and you'll well deserve it."

"Ginger," said the flour man, Wallace, "is all right in its own place. One time, I mind, I tried it —at the funeral o' an uncle o' mine who was a Rechabite; and I can tell you that so far as I was concerned that day he was sincerely mourned."

Jimmy Swan smiled blandly, and squinted again through his tumbler.

"Clean, wholesome, morally stimulatin', warmth–provokin', thirst-assuagin' —the nectar o' the gods!" he said with the eloquence of an advertisement. "What's good enough for the King and Kitchener is good enough for me. You chaps should give it a trial; it would save ye a lot o' money in aromatic lozengers."

Five minutes after the Crown Hotel commercial room was a debating club, with temperance and prohibition for its subject. Mr Swan had by far the best of the argument, since none of the rest could agree upon what constituted the particular virtues or charm of alcohol, though they were unanimous in declaring their line of business made a judicious use if it absolutely indispensable.

"I've taken up that line mysel' in my unregenerate days —and that was up to a week ago," said Jimmy; "but to tell the truth, I took a dram because I liked it; my other reasons were a' palaver."

"But human geniality," said Peter Garvie (lubricating oils), who was reputed on the road to have as little geniality as a haddock —"it wants a glass o' something stronger than ginger ale to bring men together. You couldna show your friendliness to a man unless you bought him a glass o' something."

"Ye could buy him a pair o' gallowses," suggested Jimmy, and saying so, he finished the last of his ginger ale hurriedly, and put down the glass with a bang. He had an inspiration.

A little later six quite rational representatives of well-known wholesale Glasgow houses were, incredible though it may seem, in a solemn pact to suspend the ancient treating customs of their country for a week; eschew all the alcoholic beverages, and maintain "the genial flow," as Jimmy called it, on a system more likely to benefit the sale of the goods they travelled in than standing rounds of beer or whisky-and-soda.

Two hours later M'Guire met Jimmy in the High Street, beaming with satisfaction at a well-filled book of orders; his own success that day left no excuse for grumbling.

"It's a raw, cold day," said Jimmy, rubbing his hands. "Have ye any good in your mind?"

"I don't mind if I do," said M'Guire, and absent mindedly was making for the Blue Bell hostelry.

"Na! na!" said Jimmy; "mind the pledge; there's naething'll cross my lips but a threepenny cheroot.

They went into a tobacconist's and their cheroots were hardly lighted when Jimmy said, "Hurry up and we'll hae another."

"No fears!" said the boot man firmly, "I never smoked two cigars a day in my life except on Sunday, and I wouldna smoke this one noo if it hadna cost me threepence."

"Do ye feel the genial flow yet?" asked Jimmy, as they walked along the street.

"Not a bit!" said M'Guire. "It's more like burned broon paper."

Jimmy chucked away his cigar and led him into a baker's shop.

"Two London buns, miss," said he. "The best. On draught" ; leaned one arm elegantly on the counter; said, "Well, here's to us!" and ate his bun with a fair pretence at relish. M'Guire, who was renowned for being able to eat anything at any time, was finished before him.

"Hurry up, Jimmy!" he said. "We'll jist have another one, for the good o' the house."

"All right!" said Jimmy. "Make it a small one this time, miss. No! I'll tell ye what —I'll split a parley this time, Joe; I feel that bun in my heid already."

Wallace came round the corner just as they were leaving the baker's shop.

"Ye're just in time!" said Jimmy. "An hour till the train goes and we're on the batter." He was munching the last of the parley he had shared with M'Guire, and Wallace dropped to the situation.

"What's it goin' to be?" he asked with something less than the usual convivial abandon expected with the question.

"They're no' half fly wi' their drapery shops in Fa'kirk," said Jimmy, twinkling. "They should ha'e a back-door to them. Slip in to this yin," and he led them into the premises of one of his oldest customers.

"Back again, ye see, Mr Ross," he said to the draper. "It's somebody's birthday, and we're on the fair ran-dan. What are ye goin' to have, gentlemen?"

"My shout!" said Wallace. "Give it a name."

"I think I'll just have a small pocket-hankey this time," said M'Guire, and Jimmy Swan agreed that a pocket-hankey was the very thing he was thinking of having himself.

"We'll just have another!" he said when they had got them. "Just one more hankey 'll no' do ye a bit o' harm. I'm feelin' fine! A nasty raw cold day —ye need a hankey to cheer ye up."

M'Guire, who pretended to be looking all around the floor for a spittoon, declared he couldn't find room for another handkerchief, but could be doing with a 16 collar.

"Collars all round let it be," said Jimmy, "We'll just make a night of it. But mind ye, M'Guire, you're no' to start the singin'! When it comes to collars, I'm aye proud to say I can either take them or leave them. I'm no' one o' these chaps that's nip-nip-nipping awa' at collars a' day —the ruination o' the constitution and the breakin'-up o' mony a happy home. Three White Horse collars, Mr Ross, and what'll ye take yoursel'?"

Mr Ross was a pawky gentleman himself, and had heard of the commercials' compact from the traveller earlier in the day. He turned his back on them, having put forth the collars, and scrutinised the shelves behind him with profound shrewdness.

"At this time o' day I never touch a collar," he remarked. "It doesna agree wi' me before my tea. I think, if you'll allow me, seeing it's so cold a day, I'll just have a Cardigan waistcoat, Mr Swan," and he pulled down a box of those garments.

XXVII

COUNTRY JOURNEYS

As the train pulled out of Buchanan Street Station, Slymon, the tea man, drew off a fur-lined glove and put his hand inquiringly upon the foot-warmer.

"Feel that, Mr Swan!" he remarked, indignantly, and Jimmy did so.

"It's aff the bile, at any rate," he intimated cheerfully. "Or perhaps it's a new patent kind, like one of those Thermos flasks my wife got a present of at Christmas, guaranteed to keep the heat for four-and-twenty hours. She wrapped it up in a flannel, put it in the bed, and was awfully disappointed. 'Is that your feet?' she asked me at two o'clock in the morning. 'It is not,' says I. 'Then the shop that sold John Grant that bottle swindled him; it's an ice-cream freezer,' says the mistress."

"A railway foot-warmer filled with liquid gas is no use to me," proceeded the indignant Slymon, and for the next ten minutes he said things about The True Line which would have much distressed the directors of the Caledonian Railway had they been there to hear them.

Jimmy merely buttoned his coat a little tighter, tucked his rug more carefully around his legs, and looked compassionately upon his fellow-traveller

"Man, Slymon," he remarked at last, "if you get so warm as that about the shortcomings of the Caley and every other system, you'll work yourself into a perspiration that'll open all your pores, and get your death of cold when you go out at Larbert. It's your feet that's wrong to start with. Either your boots are tight or you're wearing the wrong kind of sox, or there's something up with your circulation. Thirty years ago the railways wouldn't even pretend to give us hot-water pans, and nobody in our line died of cold feet yet that I ever heard of."

"Travelling becomes more uncomfortable every year," said Slymon irritably, and Jimmy snorted.

"Look here, Slymon!" he said, "you're making me feel old, and I don't like it. If you say travelling becomes more uncomfortable every year, I must be getting blind, or you must be thirty years younger than me, and I don't believe it. Here you are in a padded carriage —Third Class —fifty per cent better than the first we used to use in the day before the firm took on Macauslane for a managing director. There's an electric light you can read your paper by without losing the sight of an eye, a thing you always risked when even Firsts were lit by oil. Here's an air-tight window that doesn't rattle, and a ventilator that works; here's a bogey carriage running so smoothly that you could drink a cup o' tea —if you thought of it —without spilling a drop, and in the old days you couldn't take a tot from the bottom of a flask, but had to bite on the neck of it, and drink between the dunts."

"Oh, I daresay things have a bit improved in your time," said Slymon, cooling down; "but even now they might be better."

"We might be better ourselves," said Jimmy Swan. "It's a conviction of that kind that keeps me from kicking a lot of folk I meet.

"If you ask me," continued Jimmy, lighting his pipe, "there was far more fun on the road before cold feet came into fashion, and when the only kind of draught that did any harm was the kind you got in tumblers."

"Youth," suggested Mr Slymon, and Jimmy for a moment meditated.

"Ay, perhaps you're right," he said. "I sometimes envy the chaps that have it, and then again I'm vexed for them, knowing they'll never understand till it's bye what a jolly good thing it was. And whiles, again, I wonder if Youth in itself is ever half so fine as it's cracked up to be; it's maybe only nice to an old man's eye because it's out of reach. The young that have it, anyway, make an awful hash wi't. I did myself . . . But all that was nothing to do with what we started out on —travelling.

"I've been on the road since the year the women wore the Dolly Vardens —d'ye mind that song? —

'Come, dear, don't fear, let your ringlets curl,
If you're out of fashion, you better leave the world,
Your sweet and pretty face will wear a winning smile,
If you buy a hat and feather in the Dolly Varden style.'

"Half my journeys then were made on gigs and wagonettes; none of your hot-water bottles and hair-stuffed seats, and I tell you, my feet never got time to get cold. If it wasn't gigs, and taking the reins myself for half the journey because the postboy had been out all night at a kirn or a coffining; it was cargo boats that started at six o clock in the morning, and the first bell would be ringing before the Boots chapped at my door.

"I see chaps noo gaun aboot on bicycles wi' a sample box o' biscuits strapped behind," continued Jimmy, lasping into the vernacular as his feelings warmed. "They call themsel's Commercials, just like the rest o' us. I'm vexed for the chaps, do ye know; I never can see ony hope for them bein' comfortably married. It's the same wi' tea."

"Tea's done!" confessed Mr Slymon, lugubriously. "Between you and me. Everybody's selling it. I know ironmongers handling Cooper's packages. There's wholesale people going among the farmers selling 20 lb. tins at what they call a wholesale rate, and never going near a grocer. I would sooner be on the road for specs or railway tunnels. Blended tea! — that's the wheeze! 'Fine silky liquor . . . Good body . . . Rich Darjeeling flavour . . . Soupcon of Pekoe gives it character.' . . . "

"I know," said Jimmy, sympathetically. "Worse than horse-cowpin'! The ordinary man kens nae mair aboot tea than I ken aboot shortbreid. And ye canna wonder at it; tea at the best's a skiddlin' thing ye tak' to wash doon breid and butter. The honestest thing I ever saw said aboot tea was in a grocer's window in Inverness —'Our Unapproachable; 2s. 6d.' "

"Sooner be in specs, or railway tunnels," repeated Slymon, sadly.

"I see you're no very keen on a line wi' a lot o' heavy cases, onyway," said Jimmy. "Noo. I wadna care to be without any cases. It's the stuff that talks! Stick it in their e'e! When I put out my stuff in a wee bit shop in Grantown it makes it look like a bargain day in Sauchiehall Street, and the shopkeeper feels awfu' lonely and sees his place infernal bare when I pack up the traps again. So doon he claps his bonny wee order! . . . The only thing that would gie me cauld feet would be travellin' withoot my cases. There's a moral weight in them as weel as avoirdupois. Man, on the quays and at the railway stations the porters ken them. 'That's C. & M.'s,' they say —'Auld Swan.' And when they're oot in the straun in front of a country shop, it's jist like a swatch o' Buchanan Street.

"I'll admit there's whiles when they're a nuisance, and that puts me in mind o' a time in the North when I got cauld feet richt enough.

"I had just got ower three weeks' rest at Christmas and New Year, a time I always used for packin' and postin' kind reminders to my customers. There was nae Secret Commission Act then, and I tell ye I was a connoisseur at geese and turkeys, and the genuine F. & F. currant bun. I sent them by the score. I sent a hundred and twenty 'Chatter-boxes' every year for the children o' the drapery trade in the West o' Scotland. All I needed to be Santa Claus was a reindeer. Macauslane put an end to that; he found oot that maist o' the weans that got the books belanged to customers a bit behind in the ledger.

"I got up to Golspie on a Hansel Monday, did my business there in an oor or twa, and then ordered a machine for Brora. I couldna even get a barrow! Some minister was being inducted down at Dornoch, and every dacent trap in the place was aff to Dornoch wi' an elder.

" 'We could run ye up wi' a shandry-dan,' says the inn-keeper, 'but then it wouldna haud your cases,'

" 'I needna go to Brora wantin' cases,' says I. 'Shairly ye can dae something, Peter?'

" 'There's naething in the yaird that would haud your cases except the hearse,' says Peter?'

" 'Well, oot wi' the hearse!' says I, and less than twenty meenutes efter I was on the road to Dornoch, sittin' beside the driver on a hearse, and the latest lines in C. & M.'s Spring goods inside it. My jove, but it was cauld!

"We drove richt up to the shop o' auld Mr Sutherland. Doon I draps frae the dickey o' the hearse, and in I goes wi' a face like a fiddler, and asks for a yaird o' crape.

" 'Dear me! Mr Swan, wha are ye buryin' the day?' says Mr Sutherland.

" 'We're buryin' Annie,' says I.

" 'Whatna Annie?' says Mr Sutherland.

" 'Animosity,' says I —ony auld baur 'll pass in Brora —and he laughed like a young yin, though I must alloo he yoked on me later on for what he ca'd my sacrilege.

"It was the first and only time, sae far, I travelled on a hearse, and I tell ye my feet were cauld!"

XXVIII

RAISING THE WIND

Mr Swan had the counter of Cameron's shop piled high with the new season's samples of corsets, lingerie, hose, lace, ribbons, and dress material. He handled them, himself, as if they had been flowers — delicately, lovingly, caressingly, and called attention to their qualities in the ecstatic tones a dealer in pictorial art would use with a customer for Raphaels. Cameron, on the other hand —a rough, bluff, quite undraperish-looking man, who had been a baker until he came to Perth from Glasgow twenty years ago and married his cousin and her shop, had plainly no artistic pleasure in the stuff displayed by the commercial traveller; he flung it about on the counter as if it had been dough. It made the traveller squirm to see him.

"Bright colours, rich effects," said Jimmy; "that's the season's note. Look at this cerise and tango —it makes ye think o' a fine spring day and the birds whistling. It'll make up beautiful!" He tossed it tenderly into billowy folds, which showed in it the most entrancing shadows, auriferous glints, and the flush of cherries. "This stuff in stripes (we call it 'peau-depeche,' from the man that thought o't first; he was a Frenchman) —it's the finest tailorin' stuff I've ever handled, goin' to be a' the go when the King comes to the Clyde."

"Is he comin'?" Cameron asked with sudden interest.

"In July," said Jimmy. "There's a rush on flags already oot at Coatbridge. It's goin' to be a drapery summer, I can tell ye! Ye'll feel it even up in Perth."

And Cameron sighed.

"Na," said he; "we'll no' feel't in Perth. We never feel onything here but cattle shows. We just kind o' driddle on frae yin year's end to the ither, and read about splendid things in the papers. I never see ye strappin' up your boxes, Mr Swan, but I wish ye would strap me up wi' them and take me back wi' ye to Gleska."

Cameron, in twenty years, since he had left St Mungo, had never returned to it even on the shortest visit. He spoke of it now with a sentimental air, and expressed a firm intention to go down and see the gaieties of July.

"I'll see a lot o' changes on Gleska," he said. "Twenty years! It looks like a lifetime! What would ye say yoursel', Mr Swan, was changed the most in Gleska in twenty years?"

Jimmy puckered up his brows and chewed a pencil, lost in thought.

"Well," said he, "there's the picture-palaces, where ye can get everything now except a dram and a bed for the night —they'll be new to to ye. And then there's Central Station; ye've never seen the Central since they altered it, have ye?"

"No," said Cameron sadly. "What's it like, noo?"

"Oh, it's beyond words!" said Jimmy, rolling ribbons up. "Ye could put the whole o' the folk in Perth between the bookstalls, and they would just look like a fitba' team. It's got the biggest, brawest, nameliest lavatory in Europe, doon a stair, where ye can get your hair cut, and a bath for sixpence. Lots o' men go down for baths and barberin' stayin' down for hours if they think their wives are lookin' for them."

Cameron laughed. "What do ye want wi' a bath in a station?" said he.

"I've kent o't bein' used for a bank," said Jimmy; "at least it served the purpose o' a bank in a way, for it got twa chaps I ken some money when they couldna get it otherwise."

"How that?" asked Cameron.

"It happened this way. Twa packers in our warehouse —Dan MacGhie and Willie Lovatt —got on the scatter a year ago at the Gleska Fair. They spent the half o' the day goin' round the town in search of the perfect schooner that was goin' to be the last, and they found their joint resources down to a single shilling. A shilling's a lot o' money in Gleska if it's tramway rides you're buying, but it doesna go far in the purchase o' liquid joy, and they were sore distressed. A' the banks were shut, but that didna matter; they hadna any money in the banks onyway. And the notion o' goin' hame at three o'clock was naturally horrible.

"Dan MacGhie's such a fool in the packin' business, ye would fancy the only way he could think o' keepin' his socks up would be to stand on his heid, but on this occasion he was pretty 'cute. 'I'll tell ye what, Willie,' said he. 'You'll hae a nice hot bath at the Central Station.'

"'What dae I want wi' a bath?' says Willie. 'I had yin a while ago.'

"'That's all right!' says Dan. 'You'll go down and have a nice wee bath to yoursel'. It'll cost ye sixpence, and ye'll take your time. Ye'll slip your coat and waistcoat oot to me. I'll go, like lightning, and put them in a fine wee pawn for a pound, and buy ye an alpaca jacket for three-and-six, and we'll have a' the odds. See! Phizz!'

"'But ye'll be sure to come back?' says Willie. 'I have no notion o' goin' out the New City Road in my galluses.'

"'Right oh!' says Dan, and Willie went down wi' him and trysted a bath, and slips his coat and waistcoat oot to Dan.

"Dan takes the coat and waistcoat in an awfu' hurry down to Oswald Street, and into a nice wee pawn, and asks a pound on them. The man in the pawn ripes the pouches, and says he couldna gie more than seven-and-six.

"'Seven-and-six!' says Dan. 'They belang to a landed gentleman!'

"'I don't care if they belanged to Lloyd George,' says the man in the pawn, 'seven-and-six is the value, and that's no' includin' the price o' the ticket.'

"Dan took the seven-and-odd-pence-ha'penny, after switherin' a wee, and went awa' doon the stair and along Argyle Street. He was disappointed. If he bought a lustre jacket for Willie, there wasna goin' to be much left for fun. A dishonest man would have just spent the money and gone awa' hame withoot botherin' aboot Willie, but Dan MacGhie wasna a chap o' that sort; he had the true British spirit.

"He goes alang the street till he comes to a shop window where there were clocks on the instalment system. If ye paid the first instalment o' half-a-crown, ye got the nock wi' ye, the notion bein' that ye paid the other seventeen-and-six in monthly instalments. Dan goes in as bold as brass and asks to see the nock. The man produced a fair clinker, fitted up wi' an alarm that would waken ye even on a Sunday. Dan tried the alarm, and made it birl, and said he thought it would dae, although he would have preferred yin a little quicker and louder in the action. He paid down half-a-crown and signed his name and address for the rest o' the instalments, and awa' oot, like the mischief, to the Trongate.

"He went into a pawn in the Trongate and pledged the nock. 'I want fifteen shillin's on that,' says he. 'It's a Kew-tested, genuine, repeater nock, jewelled in every hole.' The pawnbroker opened it wi' a knife the same's it was an oyster, and looked inside it. 'I'll gie ten shillin's on't!' says he.

"'My mither's nock!' says Dan, and him near greetin'. 'It cost five-pound-ten the year o' the *Daphne* disaster.'

"'Half-a-quid!' says the pawnbroder; 'take it or leave it!'

"Dan took the ten shillin's; looked at the time on the pawnshop clock, and ran like a lamplighter awa' back to Oswald Street. He kent fine that Willie would be vexed waitin' in the bath a' wet.

"He goes back to the first pawn and lifted Willie's coat and waistcoat, payin' back the seven-and-six interest.

"'Ye havena been lang!' says the pawnbroker, surprised to see him.

"'No,' says Dan; 'I forgot about a funeral I'm booked for this afternoon, and I need my coat.'

"He got Willie's coat and waistcoat, and bunks awa' up to the Central Station and doon the stairs to the lavatory, and chaps the door.

"Is that you, Dan?' says Willie.

"'It is,' says Dan, and slips him in his clothes.

"'My goodness!' says Willie, 'and I was gettin' cauld! I was sure ye had forgotten all aboot me! What speed did ye come!'

"'Tip-top!' says Dan. 'I started wi' sixpence, and I've three shillin's. Come on oot and we'll have a pint!'

"That's Gleska!" said Jimmy Swan. "Oh, it's changed a lot since you were there last, Mr Cameron! And now, this shell-pink moire velours, just look at the style that's in it —"

"Ye're a terrible man," said Cameron.

XXIX

ROSES, ROSES, ALL THE WAY!

From the 1st of May till well on in October no one for years has seen Jimmy Swan in business hours without a flower in his coat lapel. Any old kind of cigar is good enough for him, though his preference runs to black Burmese cheroots that look like bits of walking-stick; but when it comes to button-holes, he is a fastidious connoisseur. If the Karl Droschki rose is ever to have a perfume, you will find that Jimmy will anticipate the florist's shops by a week or two; he likes his button-holes large and redolent, and a scented Karl Droschki the size of a rhododendron is a joy he sometimes dreams of. In town he gets his daily flower by some arrangement with commercial friends in the neighbourhood of the Bazaar; on his business journeys he is rather unhappy anywhere out of the reach of fresh carnations, sweet peas, roses, or camellias; but even there he can make shift with a spray of lilac or of wallflower culled from vases in the coffee-rooms of the hotels.

"The button-hole is getting a bit out o' fashion," he told me recently; "but I don't mind; it will aye go very well in the coat of a middle-aged commercial gentleman with the right breadth in the chest for it. Give me a clean shave and a carnation, and I feel as cheery as a chap that earns his bread by singing. A flower in the coat goes a long way to conceal yon tired feeling in the morning; it's kind o' moral pick-me-up."

"I fancy," said I, "that it's also not without some beneficial effect on business"; and Jimmy shyly chuckled.

"You may be sure o' that!" said he. "Make your button-hole big enough, and the business man behind it's almost lost to sight; there's wee shops yonder in the East End where they look on me and my carnations like a kind o' glimpse o' the country, where the mavie whistles and the milk comes from. They sniff as if it was the sea-breeze down at Millport —I tell you it puts a lot o' them in mind o' their mother's gardens! Give me that kind o' country sentiment, and I'll be busy wi' my wee bit book!"

But Jimmy was not always a wearer of *boutonnieres* and a connoisseur in cut flowers. Fifteen years ago, as he told me once, he would as soon have worn a wedding-ring or a Glengarry bonnet, and the only thing he knew about flowers was that certain ones were roses and the others weren't. His wife's pathetic struggles for bloom in a tiny front plot near the Paisley Road never, in these days, roused his slightest interest in horticulture. He is still inclined to regard flowers as a product best procured in shops, but his knowledge of them at the marketable age is now extensive. It began with an experience he had in Kirkcaldy.

For two years he had made the most valiant but unsuccessful efforts to get an order from a Kirkcaldy draper, who appeared to cherish the distressing delusion that he was well enough served by other wholesale firms than C. & M. Mr Dimister was the hardest nut Jimmy had ever tried to crack. At any hour of the day he was called on he was always too desperately busy to look at anything, and never by any luck was he to be got with a vacancy in his stock that Mr Swan could replenish.

"Man, he was a dour yin!" Jimmy said to me, narrating the circumstances. "I don't object to a dour yin in reason, for once ye nab a dour yin he's as dour to stop ye as he was to start ye; forbye it's aye a feather in your bonnet. But Dimister was a perfect he'rt-break; he had nae mair come-and-go in him than Nelson's Monument —my jove! the baurs I wasted on that man! I got the length o' jottin' the heids o' my newest stories doon in a penny diary just to be sure o' ticklin' him wi' somethiлg fresh, but devil the haet would tickle Dimister; he had nae mair sense o' humour than a jyle door. There's folk like that.

"Ye have nae idea o' the patience I showed wi' the body! I tried him on the majestic line, the same's I was sellin' peerages, and I tried him on the meek —or at least as near on the meek as I could manage wi' half a ton o' cases from C. & M. in a couple o' barrows at the door. It was a' the same to Dimister —he had nae mair interest in me than if I was selling sheep-dip or railway sleepers. I tried him wi' kirk affairs, put oot a feeler now and then on politics and gave him a' the grips in Masonry; but it was nae use: he just hotched on his stool, glowered ower his specs at me, and let me ken there was naething doin'. For a' that was in the cratur's business at the time, it wasna worth my while to bother wi' him; but my pride was up, and I swore I would have him, even if I had to take a gun to't.

"One day I asked the landlord o' the hotel I was puttin' up at where Dimister stayed, and went oot to look at the ootside o' his hoose. It was a nice enough bit villa, wi' a gairden fu' o' floo'ers and a great big greenhoose. A letter-carrier passin' told me Dimister was the champion rose-grower and tomato hand in Fife.

"'I have ye noo!' says I to mysel', and wired to my friend in the Bazaar to send me oot three o' the finest roses in Gleska by the first train, even if they cost me a pound. They came in the aifternoon —fair champions! — I stuck them in my coat and went to call on Dimister.

"'Very sorry,' he says as usual; 'I'm not needin' — and then his eyes fell on my button-hole. It was the first time I ever saw a gleam o' human interest in the body's face. His eyes fair goggled.

"'That's a good rose,' he says, and came forward and looked at them closer. 'A Margaret Dickson; splendid form!'

"'No a bad rose!' I says, aff-hand. 'It's aye worth the trouble growin' a good one when ye're at it,' and I passed them over to him wi' my compliments. Ye would hardly believe it, but he was mair pleased than many a man would be wi' a box o' cigars.

"'I didna know ye were a fancier,' says he. 'That's a first-rate hybrid perpetual.'

"'The craze o' my life!' says I, quite smart. 'What's better than a bit o' gairden and an intelligent interest in the works o' Nature?'

"'Nature!' says he, wi' a girn. 'If Nature had her will o' roses, they would a' be back at the briar or killed wi' mildew and green-fly. But I needna tell you the fecht we hae wi' the randy —you that can sport a bloom like that!'

"The lang and the short o't was that I got a first-rate order there and then frae Dimister, and promised to go to his gairden next time I was roond and give him the benefit o' my experience wi' hybrid perpetuals. Me! I didna ken a hybrid perpetual frae a horse-radish! But I had my man! And I have him yet; there's no' a draper in the East o' Scotland that's mair glad to see me. When I had a day to mysel' in Gleska I went to my friend at the Bazaar, and learned as much aboot the rose trade in a couple o' hours as would keep me gaun in talk wi' Dimister for days. I bought a shillin' book on gairdenin', laid in a stock o' seedsmen's catalogues, and noo I ken far mair aboot the rose as a commercial plant than Dimister, though I never grew yin a' my days. What's the use? What's shops for? But every time I went to Dimister's, I aye had a button-hole that dazzled him. The droll thing is that havin' a button-hole grew into a habit; I started it to get roon' auld Sandy Dimister, and noo I'd sooner go without my watch."

XXX

CITIZEN SOLDIER

Mr James Swan sat at his Saturday dinner-table, and was about to draw his customary bottle of beer, when, on reflection, he put down the corkscrew and filled up his glass with water.

"Bilious, Jimmy?" said his wife.

"No," he answered. "I'll wager there's no' a bilious man this day in the Citizen Corps. Two hour's route-merchin' on the Fenwick Road is the best anti-bilious pill I ken; if it could be put up in boxes and sold in the apothecary shops, it would fetch a guinea a dozen. But ye couldna put Sergeant Watson in a box, and he's the main ingredient o' the route-merch pill. Watson's a fine, big, upstandin' chap, and it's a treat to see him handle his legs and arms the same's they were kahouchy, and double up a hill without a pech from him, but I wish he would mind at times our corps's no' made o' gladiators or Graeco-Roman wrestlers, that we're just plain business men, off and on about five-and-forty in the shade, wi' twenty years o' tramway trevellin' and elevator lifts, and easy-chairs, bad air and beer in our constitution. It's no' to be expected we can pelt up braes on the Fenwick Road like a lot o' laddies."

"I hope you'll not hurt yoursel'," said Mrs Swan anxiously.

"Hurt mysel'! I'm sore all over! Sergeant Watson sees to that! It's no' the Madame Pomeroy treatment for the skin he's givin' us, nor learnin' us the dummy alphabet; he wouldna get a wink o' sleep this night if he thought we werena sore all over. 'The sorer ye feel,' says he, 'the sooner ye'll be fit.' I tell you he's a daisy! I never knew I had calves to my legs nor muscles to my back before I joined this army . . . My goodness, Bell, is that all the meat ye have the day? That's no' a sodger's dinner."

"At any rate," said Mrs Swan, "I never saw you looking better or eating more."

"I don't know about my looks," said Mr Swan, "and that bit doesna matter, for I suppose the Germans are no great Adonises themselves, but I wish to Peter they had my legs!" and he bent to rub them tenderly. "I've learned something in the last month, Bell, —that a body's body's no' just a thing for hangin' shirts and stockings on —the same's it was a pair o' winter-dykes. For twenty years I have been that intent on cultivatin' my intellect and the West Coast trade of C. & M., and dodgin' any kind o' physical efforts that would spoil my touch wi' the country drapers, that I was turnin' into a daud o' creash, and slitherin' down this vale o' tears as if the seat o' my breeks were soaped. Do ye ken what Watson said to me one day, just the week I joined? He saw me pechin', and had the decency to call a halt. 'Are ye all right?' says he; and I told him I had the doctor's word for it that all my internal organs were in first-rate order, and as strong as a lion's. 'Since that's the case,' says he, 'it's a pity we canna flype ye, for the ootside's been deplorably neglected.' "

"The idea!" said Mrs Swan, bridling.

"Oh, the man was right enough; a bonny job I could have made last month o' any German that came down the drive wi' his bayonet fixed to look for beer! I wouldna have the strength to hand him out a bottle. But let him try't now! —Oh, mighty! but I'm sore across the back!"

"I hope you haven't racked yourself?" his wife said, anxious again.

"The only thing I've racked's my braces. Just lie you down on your hands and toes, face down, wi' your body stiff, and see how often ye can touch the floor wi' your chin."

"Indeed I'll do nothing of the kind!" said Mrs Swan. "I don't see what good that sort of thing's going to do if you have to fight the Germans. It's surely not on your hands and toes you're going to tackle them, James Swan?"

Her huband laughed. "no," said he; "and I'm no' expectin' to have to fight them even standing on the soles o' my feet, for the only Germans ye'll see in Scotland after this'll come when their trouble's bye, wi' a pack selling Christmas toys; their whiskers'll be dyed for a disguise, and they'll call themselves Maclachlans."

"And what on earth are you drilling for?" said his wife. "I'm sure I wish you were on the road again. Since ever you were back in the shops six weeks ago, it's been nothing but darning socks for me, with your marching and parades."

Mr James Swan sighed, as he was helped to a man's size portion of the pie, which, to an appetite sharpened by his military duties, seemed quite inadequate.

"If ye want to know," said he, "I'm drilling mainly to make up the average for myself and for the country. The idea that the Black Watch and the Gordon Highlanders at a shilling or two a day per man were enough to keep us safe and let us carry on fine soft-goods businesses, allowing reasonable time for golf and football, was a slight mistake. It would have worked all right if the other chaps across the North Sea did the same, but you see they dinna. Instead of goin' in, like us, for a rare good time wi' athletic sports at half-a-crown for the grandstand seats, for tango dancin' and ke-hoi, the silly nyafs went, for a penny a day, into the army. So far as I can make out from the papers, they're all as tough as nails, and they cornered the toy trade too, and a lot o' other lines that's the inalienable right of the British business man. 'Our mistake, Maria!' said the Countess. All Britain is divided into two parts —the flabby-bellied and the fit; I don't expect to have the luck to shoot a German, but at least I'm no' goin' to be a flabby."

"Then it's just for your health you're away parading?" said Mrs Swan.

"No," said her husband. "For self-respect. Sergeant Watson's system's gey sore on the muscles for a week or two, but it's most morally elevatin'. Four weeks ago if I had attempted to lean on mysel' wi' any weight I would have crumpled up like a taper; I'm sore all over just at present, but I feel that I could take a cow by the tail and swing it round my head . . . What you want in this house, Bell, is more beef, and a more generous sense of what is meant by dinner. Are ye not aware, my dear, that a sodger gets a pound a day of beef without bone? So far as I can judge, he needs it —every ounce!"

"Man, ye're just a great big laddie!" said Mrs Swan, with a shake of her husband's shoulder.

He shook his head. "That's just the worst of it, Bell," said he; "I'm no'! The greatest luck in the world just now is to be a lad of twenty. When I was young there was hanged-all happened in the world to waken me in the morning sure that I was needed to do something: it was just, every day, a trivial wee world of business, and feeling, and playing, and sleeping; no drums nor bugles in't, and nothing big enough to bother to roll my sleeves up for a blow at . . . James Swan, Commercial Traveller . . . Sold stays! . . . There was a destiny for ye! And I go along the streets just now and see a hundred thousand men in the prime o' life who haven't the slightest notion of their luck and the chance they're missing."

"What chance?" asked Mrs Swan.

"To make a better, cleaner world of it; to help to save a nation; make themselves a name that people generations after . . . Pass the water, Bell, please."

"Are you not going to take your beer?" asked Mrs Swan.

"No," said Jimmy firmly.

"Why that?" she asked.

"Because I want to," he answered. "When we were doubling along the Fenwick Road I thought of that beer all the time. I could feel the very taste o't! But the oddest thing about Sergeant Watson's sytem is that it's learned me this — that the thing you're not particularly keen to do is the thing to do, and pays in the long-run best. So I'll just take water."